HOMEBUILDING
&RENOVATING
M A G A Z I N E
BOOK OF

HOUSE
PLANS

ovolo

HOUSE PLANS

The plans in this book have previously appeared in
Homebuilding & Renovating magazine –
Britain's best selling monthly for self-builders and renovators
(www.homebuilding.co.uk).

This edition © 2007-2016 Red Planet Publishing Ltd
Original text and illustrations © 2002-2016 Ascent Publishing Ltd
St Giles House, 50 Poland Street, London W1F 7AX

ISBN: 978-1-9059-5925-9

Printed in the UK by CPI

For more information on Ovolo books about property
and home interest please visit: www.thebuildingsite.com
email: info@redplanetzone.com or call: 01480 891777

How to get the best from this book

All of the houses and bungalows are sorted first by the number of bedrooms and then by volume (as shown by square meterage).

Traditional style

HOUSE TYPE

Icons show the exterior style of each building, either: barn; traditional or contemporary.

Barn style

Traditional style

Contemporary style

FLOOR AREA

The size of the house is quoted in square metres and square feet. Figures are rounded up or down to the nearest square metre. The square foot figure is converted from the square metre figure and rounded to the nearest square foot.

Floor area
242m²
2605ft²

NUMBER OF BEDROOMS

The number of bedrooms is not always clear cut as some rooms have an optional use. Where a bedroom is shown as having an alternative use on the plan such as bedroom/study, we have made a subjective choice. In some cases you could change room use to have more or less bedrooms.

Bedrooms
4

NUMBER OF BATHROOMS

All rooms with washing facilities are included in this figure – including downstairs shower rooms, but toilets without a shower or bath are not included.

Bathrooms
2

NUMBER OF FLOORS

This lists all the floors in a house including basements and attics with rooms designed for habitation.

Floors
2

KEY FEATURES

A quick guide designed to help you choose which plans to look at.

Key features
Kitchen/dining room
Study
Utility room
Double-height hall
Galleried landing

GARAGING

Lists how many garage places there are on the plan but excludes car port spaces.

Garaging for
2 cars

DESIGNER AND CONTACT DETAILS

Web site, e-mail address and/or phone number (where available) for the designer or building company who own the plans.

Design
Great House Co

www.ovolopublishing.co.uk
01480 891777

BUILD COST

This figure is an estimate based on three factors: house size; location (which assumes an average price); and quality/type of build (which is based on a figure between that for an excellent quality build using a builder and subbies and that for a standard quality build using a main contractor). Guide figures to work out the build cost of a home in different areas of the UK and using a wider range of different construction routes are shown on page 10.

Build cost
£217,000

COPYRIGHT

Each plan in this edition is copyright as indicated here. This means that you cannot use the plan without permission.

Contemporary style

Floor area
46m²
495ft²

Bedrooms
1

Bathrooms
1

Floors
1

Key features
Open plan living area

Garaging for
0 cars

Design
John Braid
(at Leslie R Hutt)

lhuttarchitect@btinternet.com
01463 235566

Build cost
£50,000

Design © Leslie R Hutt

Plan no. **BHP 310314**

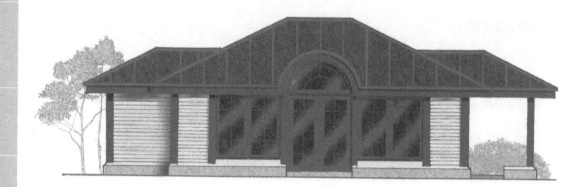

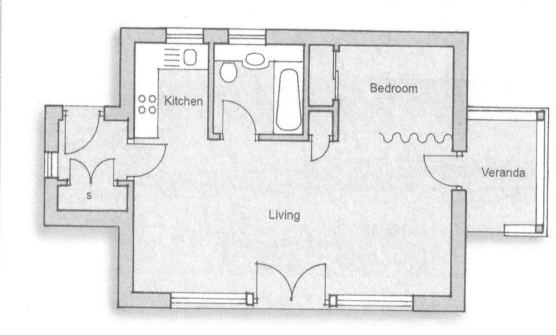

Ideal for a small plot with good views. This layout allows maximum use of the available floor space - like an individual loft apartment!

Plan no. **BHP 310035**

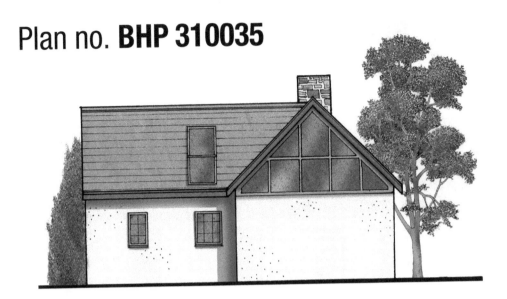

A limited plot size doesn't mean you have to put up with a cramped-feeling house. This Chaddock Design makes a small space big in two ways. First there's the open-plan layout for the living and sleeping areas, second there's the huge swathes of glass that let light wash into every part of the house.

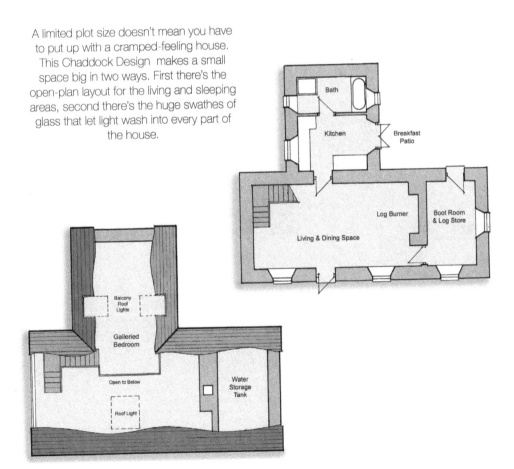

Traditional style

Floor area
65m²
700ft²

Bedrooms
1

Bathrooms
1

Floors
2

Key features
Galleried bedroom,
Boot room/log store

Garaging for
0 cars

Design
Chaddock Design

www.dreamspelldesign.co.uk
info@dreamspelldesign.co.uk
01789 459148

Build cost
£70,000

Design © Chaddock Design

Contemporary style

Floor area

85.6m²

921ft²

Bedrooms

1

Bathrooms

2

Floors

2

Key features
Full height living room
Sleeping loft en suite

Garaging for
0 cars

Design
**John Braid
(at Leslie R Hutt)**

lhuttarchitect@btinternet.com
01463 235566

Build cost
£90,000

Design © Leslie R Hutt

Plan no. **BHP 310407**

Putting a single en-suite sleeping loft into this space makes room for a lovely double-height living room that leads into a generous dining area. The kitchen could be extended with a conservatory-type breakfast room by making use of the space left by the L-shaped design.

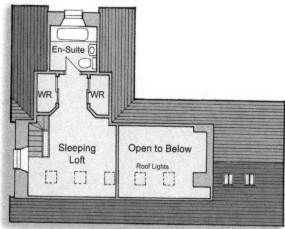

Plan no. **BHP 310740**

This house features a double-height ceiling over the kitchen and the feeling of ample space is increased by the downstairs rooms which flow into each other without interruption by walls.

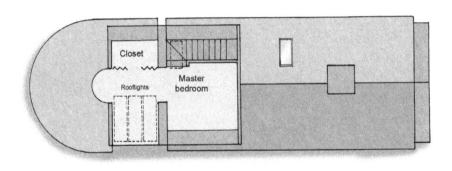

Closet

Master bedroom

Rooflights

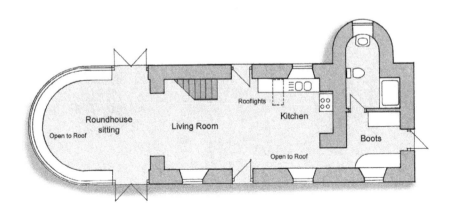

Roundhouse sitting

Open to Roof

Living Room

Rooflights

Kitchen

Boots

Open to Roof

Barn style

Floor area
110m²
1184ft²

Bedrooms
1

Bathrooms
1

Floors
2

Key features
Open plan living area

Garaging for
0 cars

Design
Jeremy Rawlings

www.periodhome.net
01884 266444

Build cost
£114,000

Design © Jeremy Rawlings

Contemporary style

Floor area
110m²
1184ft²

Bedrooms
1

Bathrooms
1

Floors
2

Key features
Open plan living area
'Green' concept

Garaging for
0 cars

Design
**John Shida
(Morningtide
Developments)**
www.morningtide.fsnet.co.uk
johnshida@morningtide.
fsnet.co.uk
01621 815485

Build cost
£114,000

Design © John Shida

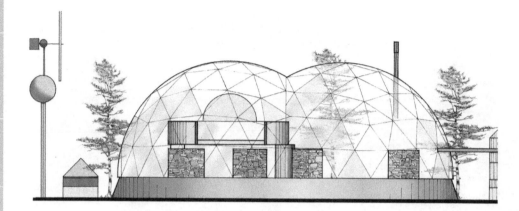

Like a scaled down Eden Project John Shida's twin-domed house allows all-round views of the surrounding area from an open-plan layout. A spiral staircase gives access to the single bedroom upstairs.

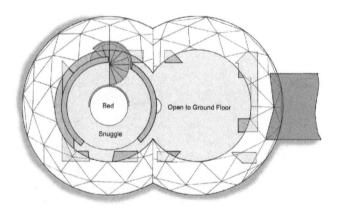

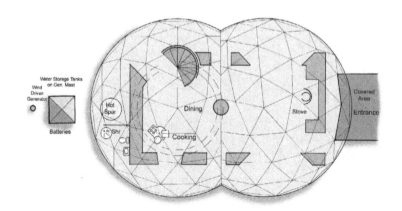

Plan no. **BHP 310767**

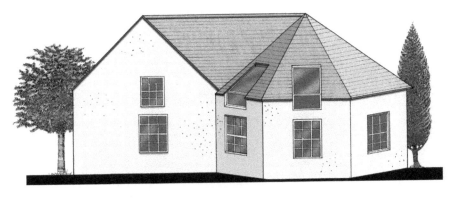

Traditional style

Floor area

110m²

1184ft²

Bedrooms

2

Bathrooms

1

Floors

2

Key features
Open plan living area

Garaging for
0 cars

Design
**JS Building
Consultancy**

www.ukbuildingconsultancy.
co.uk
jsharples@ricsonline.org
0113 250 1303

Build cost
£114,000

Design © John Sharples

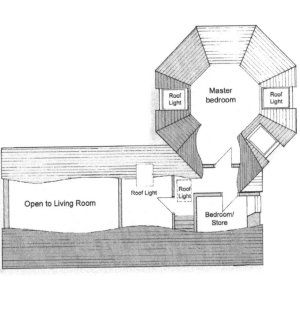

Roof Light | Master bedroom | Roof Light

Open to Living Room

Roof Light | Roof Light

Bedroom/ Store

This house provides proper open-plan living through all the downstairs rooms and a double height ceiling in the living room. The octagonal wing adds excitement to the design but doesn't remove practicality.

Utility/Store

Kitchen

Dining

Stone Hearth

Living Room

Wood Burning Stove

Contemporary style

Floor area
64m²
689ft²

Bedrooms
2

Bathrooms
1

Floors
1

Key features
Open plan living area
Shared bathroom

Garaging for
0 cars

Design
Architecture Plus

www.architecture-plus.co.uk
01934 416416

Build cost
£69,000

Design © Architecture Plus

Plan no. **BHP 310020**

A fully-glazed frontage allows great views from this single storey house with its open-plan kitchen and living area. The two bedrooms look onto a internal courtyard making this design ideal for locations where there is no view at the back of the property. A rooflight brings natural light to the bathrrom

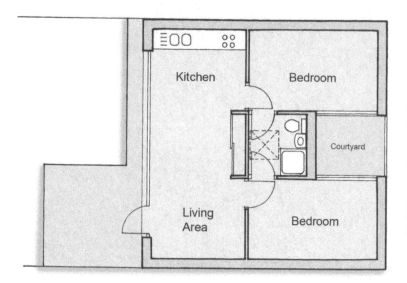

Plan no. **BHP 310059**

A small plot takes a good design to make the best out of it and this Architecture Plus house has some great ideas. The stairs have their own semi circle so they don't intrude into the open-plan ground floor. The first floor makes good use of space that would otherwise be lost to the stairwell by using it as a dressing room for the main bedroom.

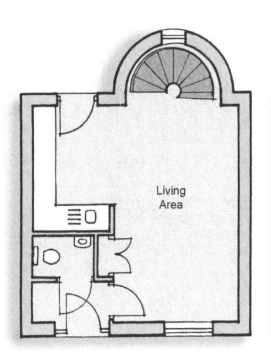

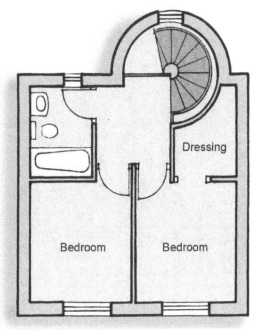

Traditional style

Floor area
67m²
721ft²

Bedrooms
2

Bathrooms
1

Floors
2

Key features
Open plan living area
Spiral staircase

Garaging for
0 cars

Design
Architecture Plus

www.architecture-plus.co.uk
01934 416416

Build cost
£69,000

Design © Architecture Plus

Traditional style

Floor area
70m²
753ft²

Bedrooms
2

Bathrooms
2

Floors
1

Key features
Kitchen/dining room
Master bed en suite

Garaging for
0 cars

Design
Churchill Design

www.churchilldesign.co.uk
info@churchilldesign.co.uk
01252 325701

Build cost
£75,000

Design © Churchill Design

Plan no. **BHP 310347**

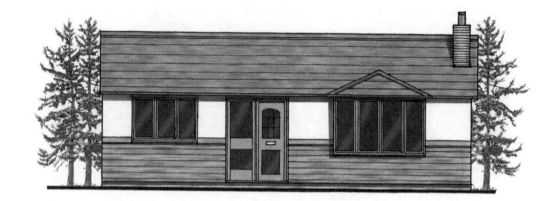

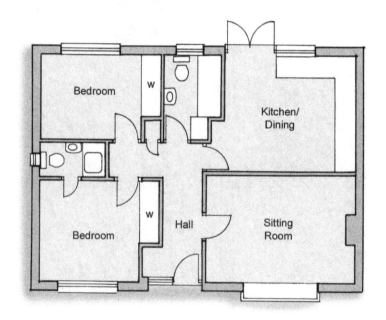

This is a fairly standard two-bed bungalow but with the added twist of an en suite shower room for the master bedroom and fitted wardrobes in both bedrooms.

Plan no. **BHP 310999**

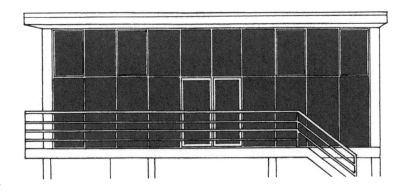

Both bedrooms and the main living area of this futuristic single storey house have direct access to the outdoors. The fully-glazed frontage makes for a well-lit kitchen while the stilt-elevated floors lift the whole house out of the ordinary in more ways than one.

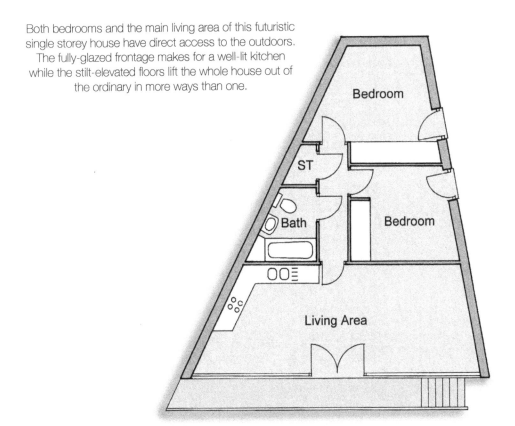

Contemporary style

Floor area
75m²
807ft²

Bedrooms
2

Bathrooms
1

Floors
1

Key features
Open plan living
Elevated construction

Garaging for
0 cars

Design
Architecture Plus

www.architecture-plus.co.uk
01934 416416

Build cost
£80,000

Design © Architecture Plus

Contemporary style

Floor area
84m²
904ft²

Bedrooms
2

Bathrooms
1

Floors
1

Key features
Vaulted living rooms
Kitchen/dining room
Porch

Garaging for
0 cars

Design
**John Braid
(at Leslie R Hutt)**

lhuttarchitect@btinternet.com
01463 235566

Build cost
£90,000

Design © Leslie R Hutt

Plan no. **BHP 310416**

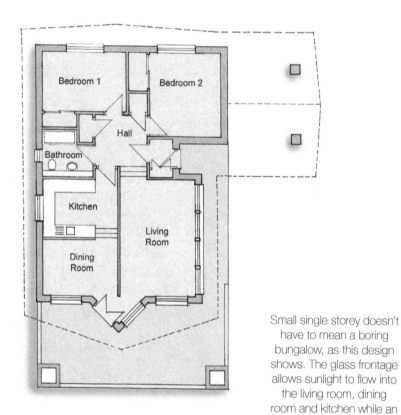

Small single storey doesn't have to mean a boring bungalow, as this design shows. The glass frontage allows sunlight to flow into the living room, dining room and kitchen while an extensive veranda provides covered seating for the patio.

Plan no. **BHP 310830**

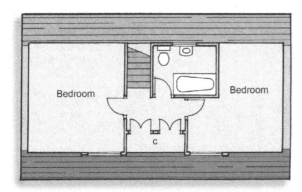

This is the perfect solution if you have a small plot that has height restriction problems. Dormer windows allow two bedrooms and a bathroom into the first floor while the combined kitchen and dining room make the best use of space downstairs.

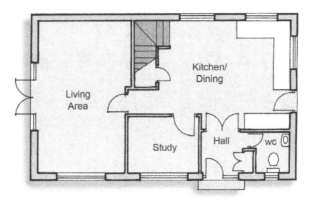

Traditional style

Floor area

88m²

947ft²

Bedrooms

2

Bathrooms

1

Floors

2

Key features
Compact design
Kitchen/dining area
Study
Hall

Garaging for
0 cars

Design
Churchill Design

www.churchilldesign.co.uk
info@churchilldesign.co.uk
01252 325701

Build cost
£91,000

Design © Churchill Design

Contemporary style

Floor area
89m²
958ft²

Bedrooms
2

Bathrooms
1

Floors
1

Key features
Kitchen/dining area
Roof lights

Garaging for
0 cars

Design
John Braid
(at Leslie R Hutt)

lhuttarchitect@btinternet.com
01463 235566

Build cost
£92,000

Design © John Braid

Plan no. **BHP 310404**

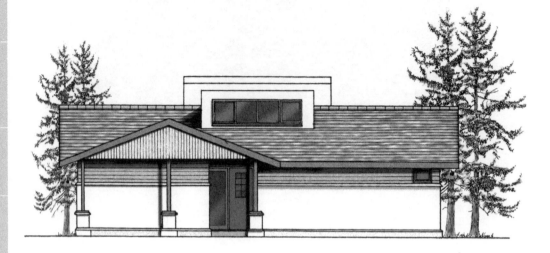

Putting a dormer window
into a single-storey house
creates loads of extra light
into the living rooms.

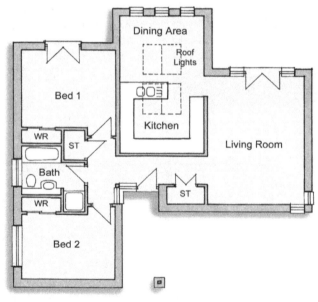

Dining Area

Roof Lights

Bed 1

WR

ST

Kitchen

Bath

Living Room

WR

ST

Bed 2

Carport

Plan no. **BHP 310026**

Traditional style

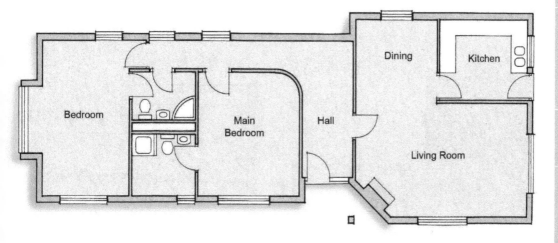

Clever use of a curved interior wall increases the size of the entrance hall, the living/dining room has triple aspect windows for maximum light and both bedrooms have en-suite facilities.

Floor area
92m²
990ft²

Bedrooms
2

Bathrooms
2

Floors
1

Key features
Living/dining area
Both bedrooms en suite
Hall

Garaging for
0 cars

Design
John Shida
(Morningtide Developments)
www.morningtide.fsnet.co.uk
johnshida@morningtide.fsnet.co.uk
01621 815485

Build cost
£95,000

Design © John Shida

Traditional style

Floor area
96m²
1033ft²

Bedrooms
2

Bathrooms
2

Floors
2

Key features
Kitchen/diner
Real fire in lounge
Master en suite
Playroom
Study

Garaging for
0 cars

Design
Architecture Plus

www.architecture-plus.co.uk
01934 416416

Build cost
£100,000

Design © Architecture Plus

Plan no. **BHP 310353**

Lots of light and a great use of space are the two key factors
in this design. There's flexibility too – the first floor rooms could
easily become an extra bedroom and en-suite bathroom great
for guests and permanent residents alike.

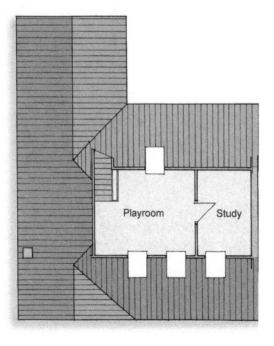

Plan no. **BHP 310350**

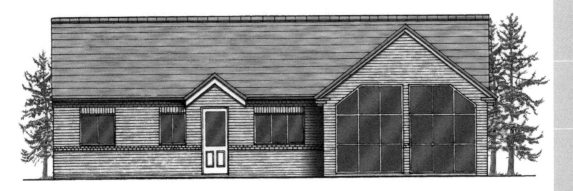

The living space flows naturally from room to room and could be open=plan or sparate (as here). The glazed wall of the lounge ensures plenty of light and would allow great views – if available.

Traditional style

Floor area
118m²
1270ft²

Bedrooms
2

Bathrooms
1

Floors
1

Key features
Linked living rooms
Full height lounge

Garaging for

Design
Eclipse Design

www.eclipsedesign.
copperstream.co.uk
enquiries@eclipsedesignuk.net
0845 460 4758

Build cost
£123,000

Traditional style

Floor area
126m²
1356ft²

Bedrooms
3

Bathrooms
1

Floors
2

Key features
Upside-down living
Full-width balcony
Veranda

Garaging for
1 car

Design
Architecture Plus

www.architecture-plus.co.uk
01934 416416

Build cost
£131,500

Design © Architecture Plus

Plan no. **BHP 310623**

This house offers upside-down living with bedrooms on the ground floor – great if you have views acceible from first floor height - as in many coastal locations.

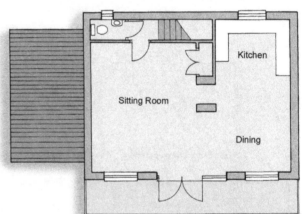

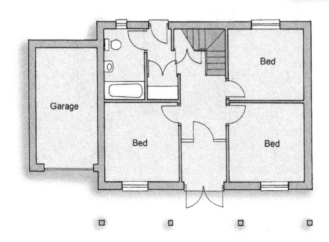

Plan no. **BHP 310458**

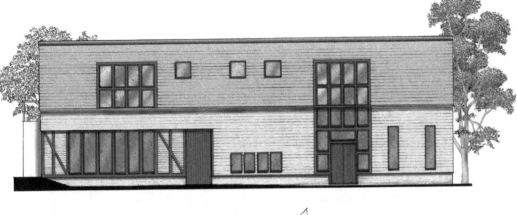

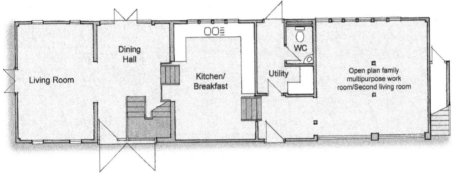

Living Room

Dining Hall

Kitchen/Breakfast

Utility

WC

Open plan family multipurpose work room/Second living room

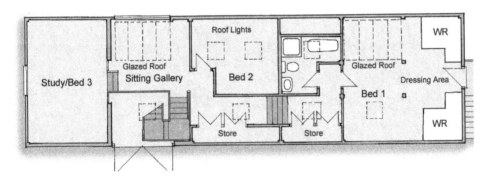

Study/Bed 3

Glazed Roof

Sitting Gallery

Roof Lights

Bed 2

Glazed Roof

Bed 1

Dressing Area

WR

WR

Store

Store

Barn style

Floor area

127m²

1367ft²

Bedrooms

3

Bathrooms

1

Floors

2

Key features
Kitchen/breakfast room
Dining Hall
Large family room
Utility room
Sitting gallery

Garaging for
0 cars

Design
Chaddock Design

www.dreamspelldesign.co.uk
info@dreamspelldesign.co.uk
01789 459148

Build cost
£132,500

The beauty of barn-style living is the opportunity to install full-height windows in parts of the build. In this Chaddock Design design the windows flood light into the dining hall and the open-plan layout makes sure that both the kitchen and living room benefit too. Upstairs expansive glazed areas over the sitting gallery and bedroom one help to bring the outside in.

Traditional style

Floor area

127m²

1367ft²

Bedrooms

2

Bathrooms

1

Floors

2

Key features
Kitchen/breakfast area
Dining room
Snug
Studio
Family room

Garaging for
0 cars

Design
**James Campbell
Associates**

01706 354888

Build cost
£132,500

Design © James Campbell

Plan no. **BHP 310761**

This house is all about wow factors. There's the link bridge over an atrium leading to a well-lit sitting room upstairs. Downstairs a sunken kitchen creates an interesting feature while the snug, dining room and family room provide loads of living space.

Plan no. **BHP 310491**

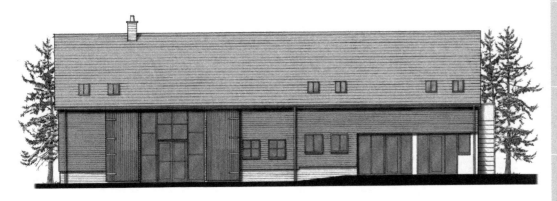

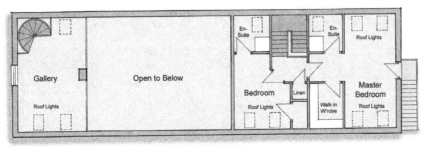

Gallery

Roof Lights

Open to Below

En-Suite

En-Suite

Roof Lights

Bedroom

Linen

Walk in W'robe

Master Bedroom

Roof Lights

Roof Lights

Utility Room

ST

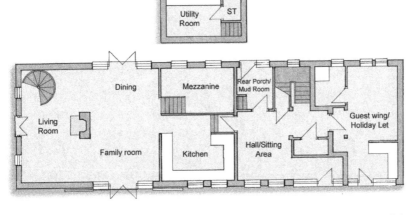

Dining

Mezzanine

Rear Porch/ Mud Room

Living Room

Family room

Kitchen

Hall/Sitting Area

Guest wing/ Holiday Let

The first floor of this design is open above the main living areas making these spaces light and airy. This design also allows for a mezzanine deck above the kitchen area. The first floor is split into two levels with an attractive gallery at one end. The guest wing can be accessed at first floor height from an external staircase. Finally, there is a semi-basement utility room accessed from the mezzanine floor.

Floor area
127m²
1367ft²

Bedrooms
2

Bathrooms
3

Floors
3

Key features
Basement utility room
Double height living area
Guest wing
Gallery
Mud room

Garaging for
0 cars

Design
John Braid
(at Leslie R Hutt)

lhuttarchitect@btinternet.com
01463 235566

Build cost
£132,500

Design © Leslie R Hutt

Barn style

Floor area
127m²
1367ft²

Bedrooms
2

Bathrooms
1

Floors
2

Key features
Open plan living area
Kitchen/dining area
Utility room
Office
Gallery/sitting area

Garaging for
0 cars

Design
Planahome

www.planahome.uk.com
plans@planahome.uk.com
01326 373600

Build cost
£132,500

Design © Planahome

Plan no. **BHP 310758**

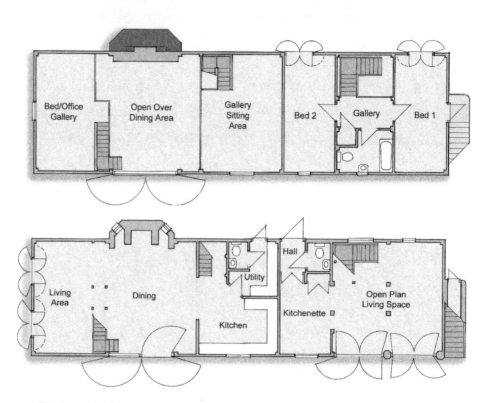

This house is all about open-plan living downstairs with excellent features like the twin galleried areas upstairs. There's also a handy annexe ideal for granny or holiday lets if you live in a tourist-friendly area.

Plan no. **BHP 310152**

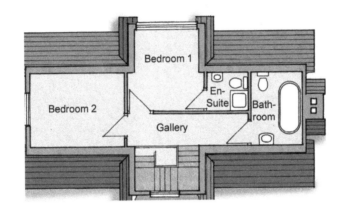

Bedroom 1

Bedroom 2

En-Suite

Bath-room

Gallery

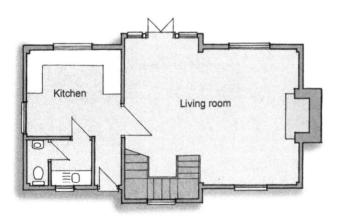

Kitchen

Living room

The full-height window on the stairwell lets light into the living and sleeping rooms. Upstairs conservation-style rooflights provide extra daylight into both bedrooms.

Floor area
136m²
1464ft²

Bedrooms
2

Bathrooms
2

Floors
2

Key features
Pen plan living area,
Galleried landing
Utility room

Garaging for
0 cars

Design
Border Oak

www.borderoak.com
sales@borderoak.com
01568 708752

**Build cost
£125,000**

Design © Border Oak

Contemporary style

Floor area

146m²

1572ft²

Bedrooms

2

Bathrooms

2

Floors

2

Key features
Multi-level living
Open-plan living
Balconies
Reception hall
Both beds en suite

Garaging for
0 cars

Design
**John Braid
(at Leslie R Hutt)**

lhuttarchitect@btinternet.com
01463 235566

Build cost
£134,000

Design © Leslie R Hutt

Plan no. **BHP 310836**

This John Braid design is a spectacular modernist sculpture you can live in. Features include an open-plan dining room, living room and kitchen. Two big bedrooms, a wealth of terraces and an attic store complete this package.

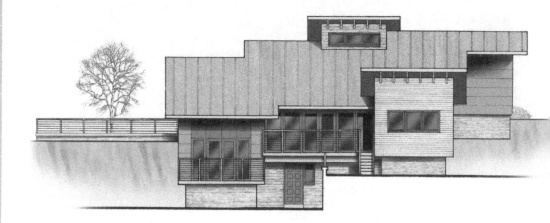

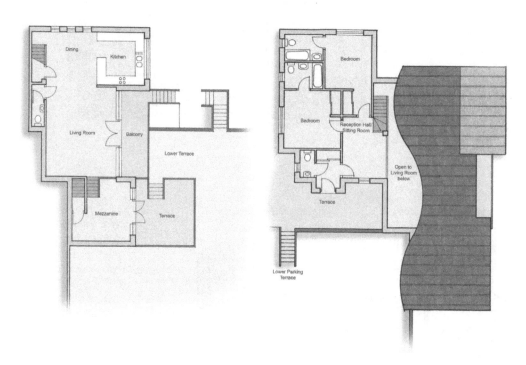

Plan no. **BHP 310833**

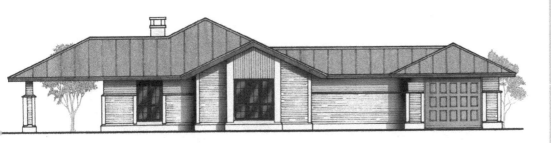

This bungalow has some unusual features like the multi-windowed wall on the dining and living room, a vast master bedroom suite and a galley kitchen with direct access to the outside. From the plan view you can see how well this design could frame a beautiful garden in the L-shape created by the garage and the main body of the house.

Floor area

149m²

1604ft²

Bedrooms

2

Bathrooms

2

Floors

2

Key features
Living/dining room
Master en suite
Feature fireplace
Car port

Garaging for
1 car

Design
**John Braid
(at Leslie R Hutt)**

lhuttarchitect@btinternet.com
01463 235566

Build cost
£137,000

Design © Leslie R Hutt

Traditional style

Floor area
160m²
1722ft²

Bedrooms
2

Bathrooms
1

Floors
2

Key features
Dining hall
Galley kitchen

Garaging for
0 cars

Design
**John Shida
(Morningtide
Developments)**
www.morningtide.fsnet.co.uk
johnshida@morningtide.
fsnet.co.uk
01621 815485

Build cost
£147,000

Design © John Shida

Plan no. **BHP 310164**

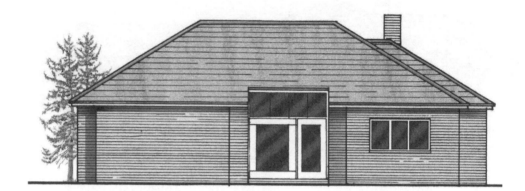

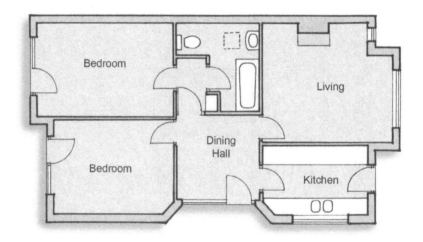

This bungalow has big rooms and space for luxuries like a dining hall off
the galley kitchen. Both bedrooms get their own access to the garden.

Plan no. **BHP 310248**

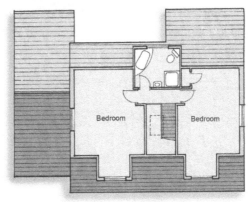

Bedroom

Bedroom

Utility

Dining

Kitchen

Garage

Sitting Room

Study

Clks

The kitchen, dining room and sitting room flow into each other while upstairs two double bedrooms share a large family bathroom. The garage can be accessed from within the house via the lobby between the kitchen and utiliity room.

Traditional style

Floor area
170m²
1830ft²

Bedrooms
2

Bathrooms
1

Floors
2

Key features
Kitchen/dining room
Utility room
Study

Garaging for
1 car

Design
Churchill Design

www.churchilldesign.co.uk
info@churchilldesign.co.uk
01252 325701

£

Build cost
£156,400

Design © Churchill Design

Traditional style

Floor area
203m²
2185ft²

Bedrooms
2

Bathrooms
2

Floors
2

Key features
Utility room
Study
Master bed en suite
Dining hall

Garaging for
0 cars

Design
Custom Homes

www.customhomes.co.uk
admin@customhomes.co.uk
01787 377388

Build cost
£187,000

Design © Custom Homes

Plan no. **BHP 310245**

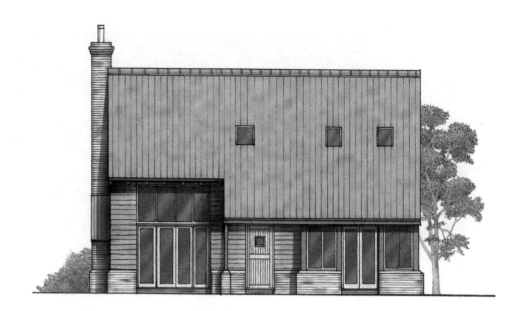

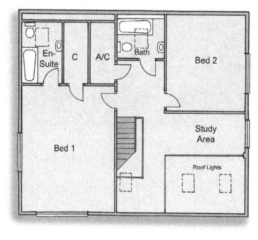

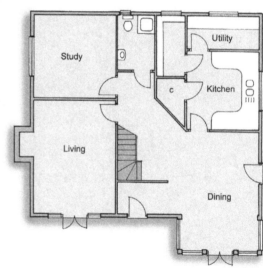

The entrance to this house opens into an open-plan dining room that leads through to a big living room and study. Putting two bedrooms upstairs leaves loads of space for an en-suite bathroom off bedroom one and a study area (which overlooks the double-height dining room) beside bedroom two.

Plan no. **BHP 310464**

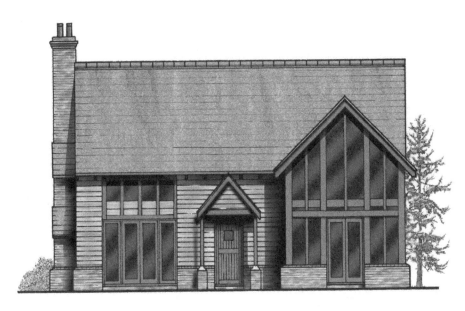

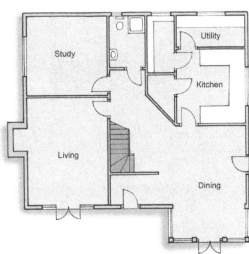

Contemporary style

Floor area
203m²
2185ft²

Bedrooms
2

Bathrooms
2

Floors
2

Key features
Double-height dining
Utility room
Master en suite

Garaging for
0 cars

Design
Custom Homes

www.customhomes.co.uk
admin@customhomes.co.uk
01787 377388

Build cost
£192,000

Design © Custom Homes

The cathedral window isn't the only striking feature of this design, but it does flood light into the dining hall. If desired the kitchen could be opened up to create a large kitchen/dining area. The addition of a pantry is also a neat touch. Upstairs the two bedrooms are both large and have a bathroom each.

Contemporary style

Floor area
214m²
2303ft²

Bedrooms
3

Bathrooms
2

Floors
2

Key features
Living/dining room
Sunken den
Guest living area
Feature landing bridge

Garaging for
0 cars

Design
Jeremy Rawlings

www.periodhome.net
01884 266444

Build cost
£197,000

Design © Jeremy Rawlings

Plan no. **BHP 310110**

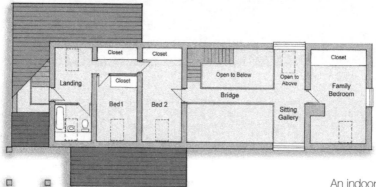

An indoor bridge, a sunken den and extensive glazing make this home an exciting proposition. There's a self-contained annexe for guests – and two staircases.

Plan no. **BHP 310818**

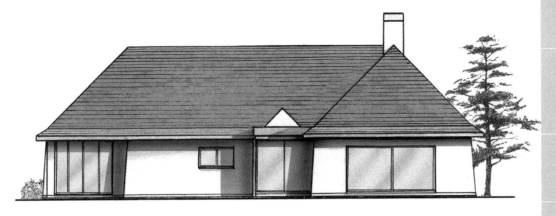

Display

Hall

WC

Double Garage

Study/Reading Room Over

Bedroom

Bath

Bath

Bedroom

Display

Kitchen

Breakfast

Dining

Low wall

Roof Light

Exp. Truss Over

TV/Living

This is a flexible single storey design with plenty of open space. The two bedrooms have an en-suite each and are accessed by a window-packed corridor that's flooded with natural light. The dining and living rooms are designed as one and lead through to the kitchen with a door to the large unattributed space over the double garage.

Traditional style

Floor area
227m²
2443ft²

Bedrooms
2

Bathrooms
2

Floors
2

Key features
Living/dining area
Kitchen/breakfast bar
Both beds en suite
First floor study

Garaging for
2 cars

Design
**John Shida
(Morningtide
Developments)**
www.morningtide.fsnet.co.uk
johnshida@morningtide.
fsnet.co.uk
01621 815485

Build cost
£204,000

Design © John Shida

Traditional style

Floor area

82m²

883ft²

Bedrooms

3

Bathrooms

1

Floors

2

Key features
Kitchen/dining area

Garaging for
0 cars

Design
Architecture Plus

www.architecture-plus.co.uk
01934 416416

Build cost
£88,000

Design © Architecture Plus

Plan no. **BHP 310062**

A compact design for
a narrow plot which
squeezes in three
bedrooms and a
kitchen/dining area.

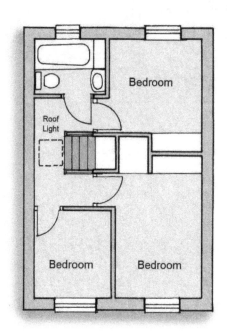

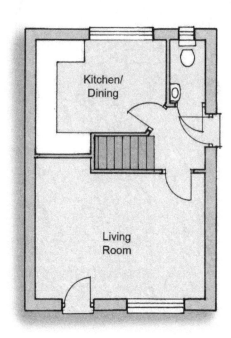

Plan no. **BHP 310968**

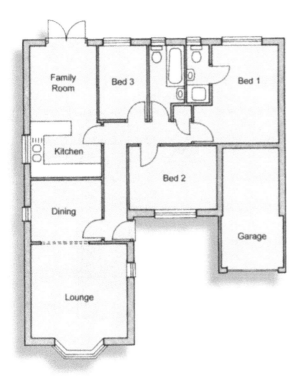

There's a good-sized kitchen and family room, a separate dining room and lounge. The master bed has an en suite and there's even a single garage in this compact design.

Traditional style

Floor area
90m²
969ft²

Bedrooms
3

Bathrooms
2

Floors
1

Key features
Lounge/diner
Kitchen/family room
Master en suite

Garaging for
1 car

Design
Planahome

www.planahome.uk.com
plans@planahome.uk.com
01326 373600

Build cost
£97,500

House design
© Planahome

Traditional style

Floor area
90m²
969ft²

Bedrooms
3

Bathrooms
3

Floors
2

Key features
Living/dining room
Kitchen bay window
Master en suite

Garaging for
0 cars

Design
Eclipse Design

www.eclipsedesign.cop-
perstream.co.uk
enquiries@eclipsedesignuk.net
0845 460 4758

Build cost
£94,000

Design © Eclipes Design

Plan no. **BHP 310845**

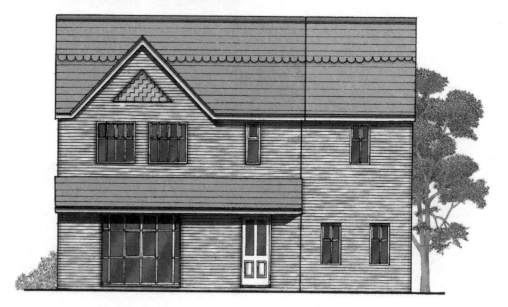

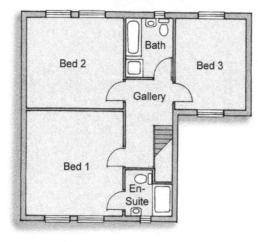

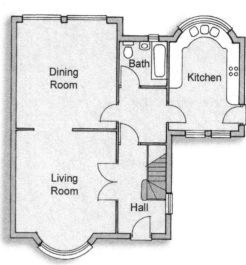

This L-shaped house makes great use of space with its three bedrooms and generous living rooms. Put in foundations at the time of building and you could easily fill in the 'L' at a later date with a family room attached to the kitchen and an en suite accessed through the front window of bedroom 3.

Plan no. **BHP 310857**

Kitchen/
Breakfast

Dining

Bedroom

Bedroom

Living Room

ST

W

Porch

W

Bedroom

This single storey home is split equally into living and sleeping spaces. The dining and living rooms are open plan while the kitchen/breakfast room has direct access to the garden. Across the hall there are two double bedrooms, one single and two bathrooms.

Traditional style

Floor area
93m²
1001ft²

Bedrooms
3

Bathrooms
2

Floors
1

Key features
Linked living/dining
Master en suite
Porch

Garaging for
0 cars

Design
Planahome

www.planahome.uk.com
plans@planahome.uk.com
01326 373600

Build cost
£96,000

Design © Planahome

Traditional style

Floor area
98m²
1055ft²

Bedrooms
3

Bathrooms
1

Floors
2

Key features
Kitchen/dining room
Separate living room

Garaging for
0 cars

Design
Churchill Design

www.churchilldesign.co.uk
info@churchilldesign.co.uk
01252 325701

Build cost
£102,000

Design © Churchill Design

Plan no. **BHP 310809**

This is a simple, stylish design that makes the best of a small site. The combined kitchen and dining room create a good-size living area across the back of the house. Upstairs the master bedroom is a good size and has its own bay window.

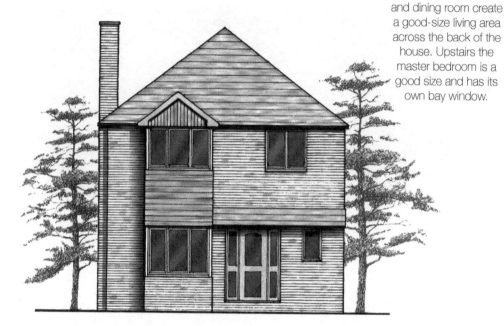

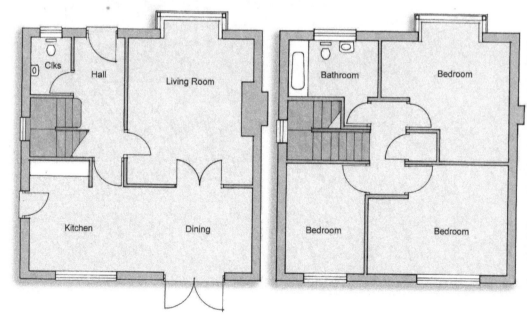

Plan no. **BHP 310086**

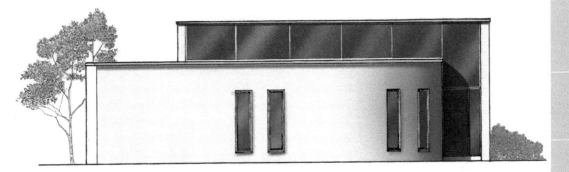

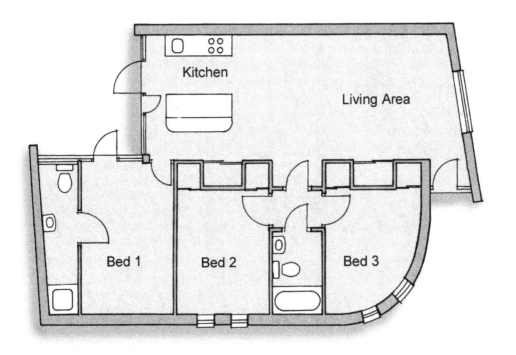

Kitchen

Living Area

Bed 1

Bed 2

Bed 3

A cool modern take on the three-bedroom house cleverly worked into a single storey. A good design for a site where the views are limited as the master bedrrom/kitchen could open onto a courtyard.

Traditional style

Floor area
111m²
1195ft²

Bedrooms
3

Bathrooms
1

Floors
2

Key features
Narrow design
Kitchen/dining
Bedroom balcony
Laundry room

Garaging for
0 cars

Design
Peter King

info@carden-king.co.uk
01367 253330

Build cost
£115,000

Design © Peter King

Plan no. **BHP 310044**

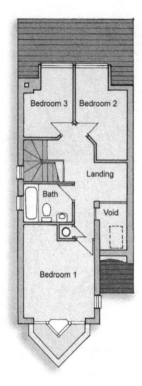

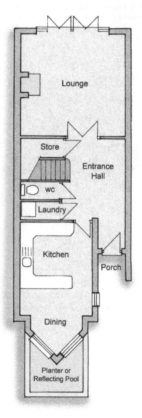

A narrow site doesn't mean you have to skimp on great living space. A Velux-type window lights the entrance hall that doubles back into a large kitchen and forward into a generous lounge. Upstairs, the biggest bedroom gets a triangular balcony.

Plan no. **BHP 310680**

This design will take advantage of a long, narrow plot. It uses the space above the carport for an extra bedroom and a big family bathroom which frees up space for two further bedrooms on the first floor and a long living/dining room downstairs.

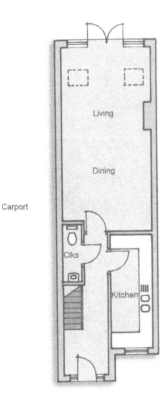

Living

Dining

Carport

Clks

Kitchen

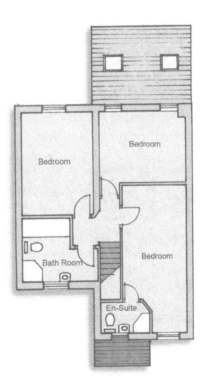

Bedroom

Bedroom

Bath Room

Bedroom

En-Suite

Traditional style

Floor area
115m²
1238ft²

Bedrooms
3

Bathrooms
2

Floors
2

Key features
Narrow design
Living/dining room
Car port
Master en suite
Galley kitchen

Garaging for
0 cars

Design
Churchill Design

www.churchilldesign.co.uk
info@churchilldesign.co.uk
01252 325701

Build cost
£120,000

Traditional style

Floor area
117m²
1259ft²

Bedrooms
3

Bathrooms
1

Floors
2

Key features
Living/dining room
Hall
Internal garage access

Garaging for
1 car

Design
**John Shida
(Morningtide
Developments)**
www.morningtide.fsnet.co.uk
johnshida@morningtide.
fsnet.co.uk
01621 815485

Build cost
£121,000

Design © John Shida

Plan no. **BHP 310005**

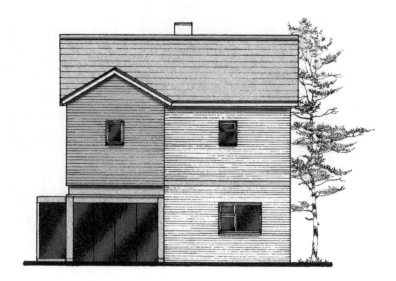

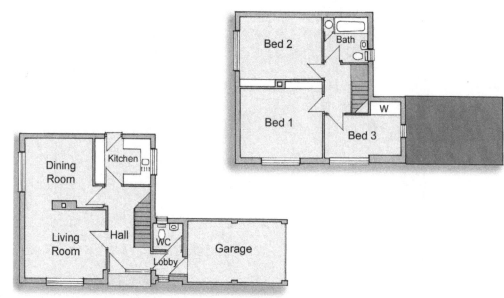

By putting the garage at
the front the width of this
house has been kept to a
minimum making it suitable
for narrower sites.

Plan no. **BHP 310914**

The full-length living room is a strong feature and if you wanted a kitchen/dining room these two rooms could be combined. Upstairs the master bed is also a good sze.

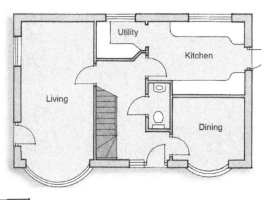

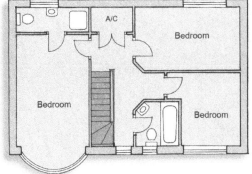

Traditional style

Floor area
127m²
1367ft²

Bedrooms
3

Bathrooms
2

Floors
2

Key features
Kitchen/dining room
Utility room
Master en suite

Garaging for
0 cars

Design
**Opus Architecture
and Design**

01252 861759

Build cost
£132,500

Plan no. **BHP 310116**

The detailing over the windows and simple porch give this simple design the look of a cottage. Inside there is a sensible kitchen/dining room and a decent size en suite bedroom.

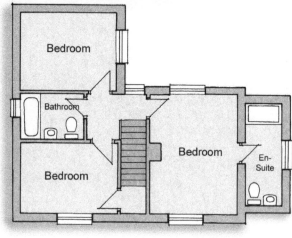

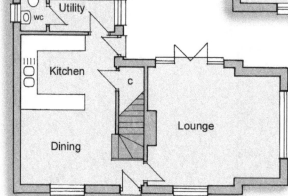

Plan no. **BHP 310938**

This house offers some nice details such as larder (for food storage) off the utility room as well as a separate study and galleried landing.

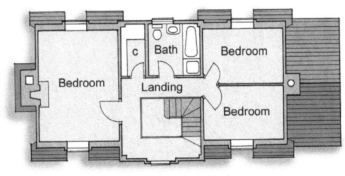

Bedroom · c · Bath · Bedroom · Landing · Bedroom

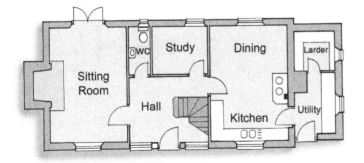

WC · Study · Dining · Larder · Sitting Room · Hall · Kitchen · Utility

Floor area
127m²
1367ft²

Bedrooms
3

Bathrooms
1

Floors
2

Key features
Kitchen/diner
Utility room
Larder
Study
Galleried landing

Garaging for
0 cars

Design
Border Oak

www.borderoak.com
sales@borderoak.com
01568 708752

Build cost
£132,500

Design © Border Oak

Traditional style

Floor area
128m²
1378ft²

Bedrooms
3

Bathrooms
2

Floors
2

Key features
Kitchen/breakfast room
Dining room
Master en suite

Garaging for
0 cars

Design
Potton

www.potton.co.uk
contact@potton.co.uk
01767 676 400

Build cost
£133,500

Design © Potton

Plan no. **BHP 310398**

Inside the hall leads off into a sizeable kitchen/breakfast room and living room. Upstairs there's a gallery landing an ensuite to the master and plenty of storage in each of the three bedrooms.

Plan no. **BHP 310383**

Overhanging eaves and jutting dormer windows give this design real character. with varying roof lines and interesting details such as the exposed rafter feet.

Bedroom

Bedroom

Bedroom

Kitchen

Sitting Room

Utility

wc

Study

Hall

c

c

Traditional style

Floor area
134m²
1442ft²

Bedrooms
3

Bathrooms
2

Floors
2

Key features
Utility room
Study
Master en suite

Garaging for
0 cars

Design
Border Oak

www.borderoak.com
sales@borderoak.com
01568 708752

Build cost
£123,000

Traditional style

Floor area
136m²
1464ft²

Bedrooms
3

Bathrooms
2

Floors
2

Key features
Utility
Separate dining room
Master en suie
Balcony bedroom 2

Garaging for
0 cars

Design
**John Shida
(Morningtide
Developments)**
www.morningtide.fsnet.co.uk
johnshida@morningtide.
fsnet.co.uk
01621 815485

Build cost
£125,000

Plan no. **BHP 310209**

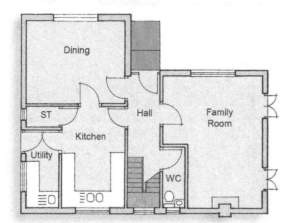

This design offers three good-sized bedrooms, one en-suite and easy access for all to the shared bathroom. The second bedroom gets its own balcony that creates a porch below.

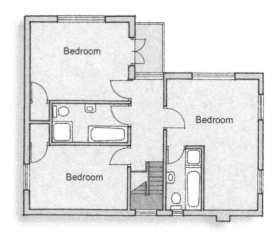

Plan no. **BHP 310215**

This design has all the external styling cues you would expect in a thatched cottage including oak lintels and eyebrow dormers. These are combined with modern touches including a large kitchen, a full-depth lounge and a good size master bedroom suite.

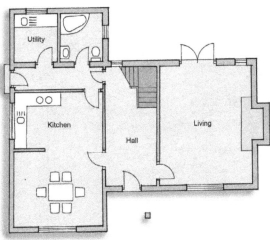

Utility

Kitchen

Hall

Living

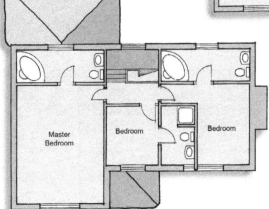

Master Bedroom

Bedroom

Bedroom

Traditional style

Floor area
137m²
1475ft²

Bedrooms
3

Bathrooms
3

Floors
2

Key features
Kitchen/dining room
Utility room
All beds en suite

Garaging for
0 cars

Design
JS Building Consultancy

www.ukbuildingconsultancy.co.uk
jsharples@ricsonline.org
0113 250 1303

Build cost
£126,000

Traditional style

Floor area
139m²
1496ft²

Bedrooms
3

Bathrooms
2

Floors
2

Key features
Kitchen/Diner
Utility room
Car port
Master en suites

Garaging for
0 cars

Design
Churchill Design

www.churchilldesign.co.uk
info@churchilldesign.co.uk
01252 325701

Build cost
£128,000

Design © Churchill Design

Plan no. **BHP 310872**

This traditional dormer window cottage features a full-depth sitting room and master bedroom above. There's also an open-plan dining and kitchen area and a useful utility space. Smart packaging makes room for two more bedrooms, an en-suite and a family bathroom on the first floor.

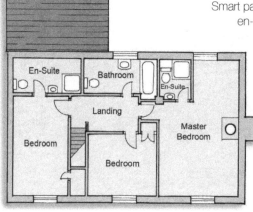

Plan no. **BHP 310506**

This country cottage has a large lounge and an L-shaped master bedroom suite. This frees up space in the rest of the house for a splendid kitchen/dining space, a study and two more double bedrooms.

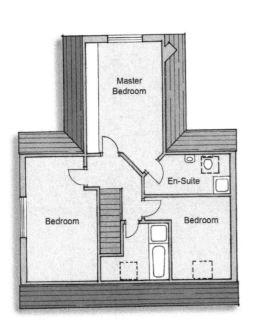

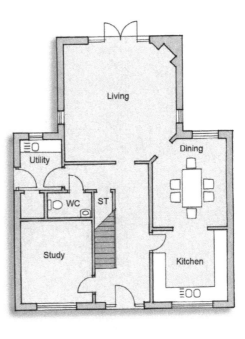

Traditional style

Floor area
140m²
1507ft²

Bedrooms
3

Bathrooms
2

Floors
2

Key features
Kitchen/dining room
Utility room
Study
Master en suite

Garaging for
0 cars

Design
Ormerod Design Group

odg@ormeroddesign.co.uk
0113 289 3763

Build cost
£129,000

Traditional style

Floor area
140m²
1507ft²

Bedrooms
3

Bathrooms
3

Floors
2

Key features
Kitchen/dining room
Living with inglenook
Sitting hall
All beds en suite

Garaging for
0 cars

Design
Jeremy Rawlings

www.periodhome.net
01884 266444

Build cost
£129,000

Plan no. **BHP 310530**

The lounge, with its massive inglenook fireplace, takes centre stage in this design with all the first floor rooms flowing off it. A single flight of stairs leads up to the galleried landing that goes through to an L-shaped master suite and two en-suite bedrooms.

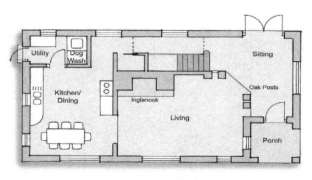

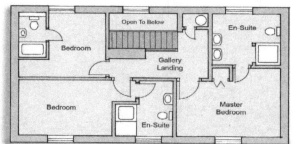

Plan no. **BHP 310272**

Good use of dormer windows give the first floor of this house extra dayllight where it's most needed – over the landing and in both bathrooms. Other features include a utility room and a full-depth sitting room with twin French doors.

Contemporary style

Floor area
140m²
1507ft²

Bedrooms
3

Bathrooms
2

Floors
2

Key features
Utility room
Separate dining room
Master en suite

Garaging for
0 cars

Design
County Contracts

countycontractsltd@
fsmail.net
01892 785153

Build cost
£129,000

Design © County Contracts

Contemporary style

Floor area
142m²
1528ft²

Bedrooms
3

Bathrooms
3

Floors
2

Key features
Dining hall
Utility room
Master en suite

Garaging for
0 cars

Design
Design 62

01484 300843

Build cost
£130,500

Design © Design 62

Plan no. **BHP 310794**

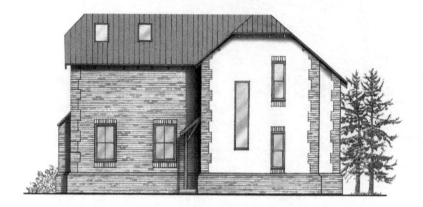

This combines double-height glazing and open-plan spaces with traditional elements including vaulted ceilings in the master and second bedroom.

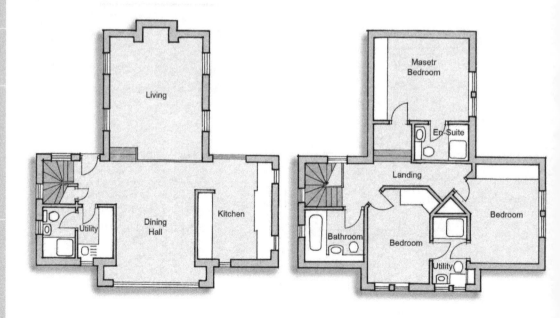

Plan no. **BHP 310935**

Barn style

Floor area
144m²
1550ft²

Bedrooms
3

Bathrooms
2

Floors
2

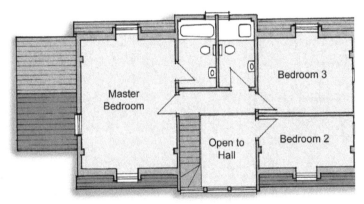

Master Bedroom

Bedroom 3

Open to Hall

Bedroom 2

Want to live in a barn but can't find one to convert? The easy solution is to build this instant barn from Border Oak. Great features include the double height windows that flood daylight into the expansive hall. Three good-sized bedrooms are accessed from the first floor galleried landing.

Key features
**Dining hall
Utility/study
Master en suite**

Garaging for
0 cars

Design
Border Oak

www.borderoak.com
sales@borderoak.com
01568 708752

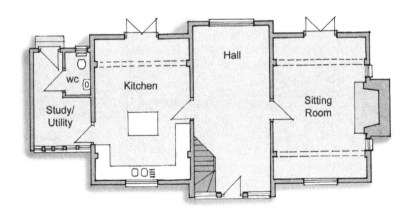

Hall

wc

Kitchen

Study/ Utility

Sitting Room

Build cost
£132,500

Design © Border Oak

Traditional style

Floor area
149m²
1615ft²

Bedrooms
3

Bathrooms
3

Floors
2

Key features
1st floor open plan living
Feature fireplace
Study
Master en suite

Garaging for
1 car

Design
Architecture Plus

www.architecture-plus.co.uk
01934 416416

Build cost
£137,000

Design © Architecture Plus

Plan no. **BHP 310956**

With sleeping space on the ground floor and living space up top this house is designed to take advantage of great views. The open-plan dining, kitchen and sitting room leads onto a full-width balcony. The study with its en-suite bathroom could easily become a self-contained guest suite.

Plan no. **BHP 310326**

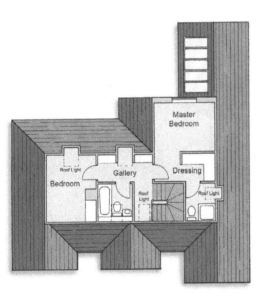

Incorporating the garage door into one of the bays on this double–fronted design makes for a neat, symmetrical façade. Up the steps and through the hall there's an L-shaped kitchen, dining and sun lounge area plus a large living room and guest suite. Upstairs there's a full-depth master suite and a good-sized second bedroom.

Traditional style

Floor area
150m²
1615ft²

Bedrooms
3

Bathrooms
3

Floors
2

Key features
Kitchen/dining room
Sun lounge
Guest suite
Master en suite

Garaging for
1 car

Design
Design & Materials

www.designandmaterials.uk.com
enquiries@designandmateria
ls.uk.com
01909 540 123

Build cost
£138,000

Design © Design &
Materials

Traditional style

Floor area

150m²

1615ft²

Bedrooms

3

Bathrooms

2

Floors

2

Key features
Family room
Study
Utility room
Master en suite

Garaging for
0 cars

Design
Custom Homes

www.customhomes.co.uk
admin@customhomes.co.uk
01787 377388

Build cost
£138,000

Plan no. **BHP 310671**

This design squeezes the maximum living and sleeping area out of a relatively small plot but all the room sizes remain large and comfortable. Virtually any building material combination could be used to suit the surrounding environment.

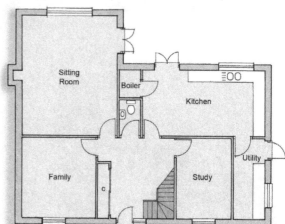

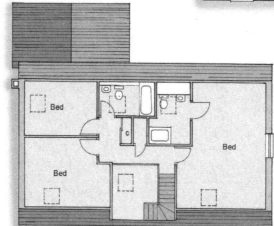

Plan no. **BHP 310557**

Traditional style

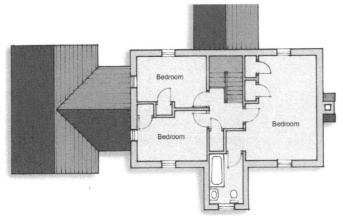

Off the hall there's an open-plan kitchen/dining room a large living room and a bathroom. Upstairs the master suite takes up one side of the house and has its own bathroom built into the central gable.

Floor area
152m²
1636ft²

Bedrooms
3

Bathrooms
2

Floors
2

Key features
Kitchen/dining room
Utility room
Porch
Cellar

Garaging for
1 cars

Design
John Braid
(at Leslie R Hutt)

lhuttarchitect@btinternet.com
01463 235566

Build cost
£140,000

Design © Leslie R Hutt

Traditional style

Floor area
154m²
1658ft²

Bedrooms
3

Bathrooms
2

Floors
2

Key features
Utility room
Study
Separate dining room
Master en suite

Garaging for
0 cars

Design
County Contracts

countycontractsltd@fsmail.net
01892 785153

Build cost
£141,500

Plan no. **BHP 310725**

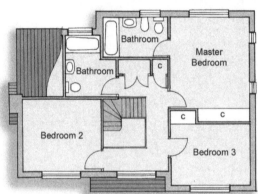

This great three-bedroom house is pretty spacious as standard but there's plenty more to come – just look at that roof. With a pair of Velux-type or dormer windows the attic area could become an extra bedroom with ease.

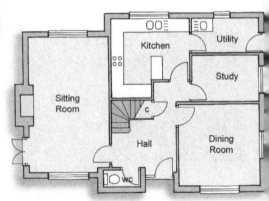

Plan no. **BHP 310401**

Contemporary style

This beautiful modern design puts the living quarters on the first floor and the sleeping space below. That means you can benefit from a great view during the day and tuck yourself into the cosy, well-equipped ground floor at night. Great touches include a first floor terrace and balcony, a bathroom per bedroom and a sunpipe-lit stairwell.

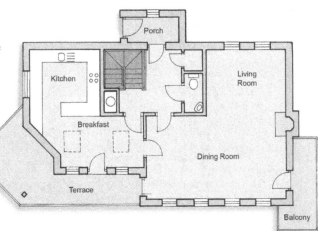

Porch · Kitchen · Breakfast · Living Room · Dining Room · Terrace · Balcony

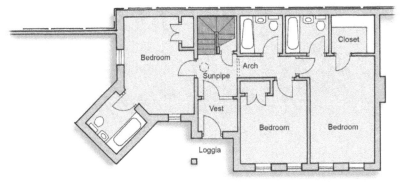

Bedroom · Sunpipe · Arch · Closet · Vest · Bedroom · Bedroom · Loggia

Floor area
155m²
1668ft²

Bedrooms
3

Bathrooms
3

Floors
2

Key features
Kitchen/breakfast room
Lounge/dining room
Porch
Master en suite
2nd en suite

Garaging for
0 cars

Design
John Braid
(at Leslie R Hutt)

lhuttarchitect@btinternet.com
01463 235566

Build cost
£142,500

Traditional style

Floor area
156m²
1679ft²

Bedrooms
3

Bathrooms
2

Floors
2

Key features
Kitchen/breakfast room
Utility room
Study
Master en suite

Garaging for
1 car

Design
Stephen Mattick

www.mattick.co.uk
mattick@mattick.co.uk
01223 891159

Build cost
£143,500

Design © Stephen Mattick

Plan no. **BHP 310683**

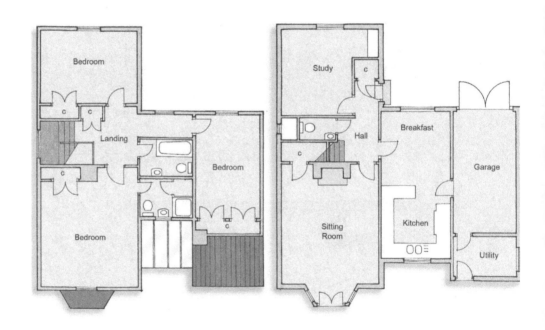

This design would look equally at home in a country or seaside location with its handsome weatherboard facing and soaring roofline. The bay-windowed sitting room and glazed-roof kitchen are great character features as is the enormous main bedroom with its built-in wardrobes and bathroom.

Plan no. **BHP 310089**

Traditional style

Floor area
157m²
1690ft²

Bedrooms
3

Bathrooms
1

Floors
2

Adding an octagonal room onto the L-shape of this three-bedroom house adds a useful space for relaxation. Alternatively this could make a brilliant feature kitchen. The circular stairway leads up to a long landing and two first floor bedrooms while the large master suite takes up a whole corner of the ground floor.

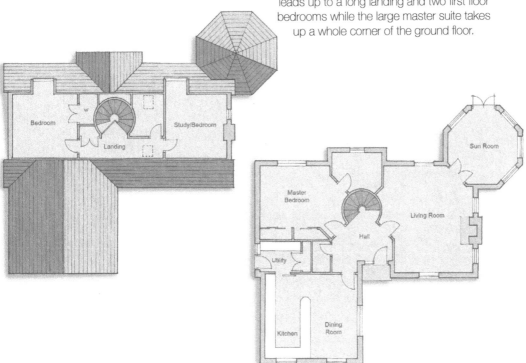

Key features
Kitchen/dining room
Circular staircase
Octagonal sunroom
Master en suite

Garaging for
0 cars

Design
The Border Design Centre

www.borderdesign.co.uk
borderdesign@btconnect.com
01578 740218

Build cost
£144,000

Traditional style

Floor area
157m²
1690ft²

Bedrooms
3

Bathrooms
2

Floors
1

Key features
Separate dining room
Utility room
Larder
Master en suite

Garaging for
0 cars

Design
The Border Design Centre

www.borderdesign.co.uk
borderdesign@btconnect.com
01578 740218

Build cost
£144,000

Plan no. **BHP 310566**

The shape of this palatial bungalow forms a central courtyard that can be accessed from the hall, kitchen and the utility room. So it's an ideal spot for a hot tub, kitchen garden and a washing line too.

Plan no. **BHP 310239**

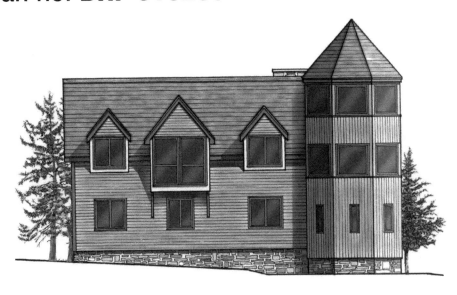

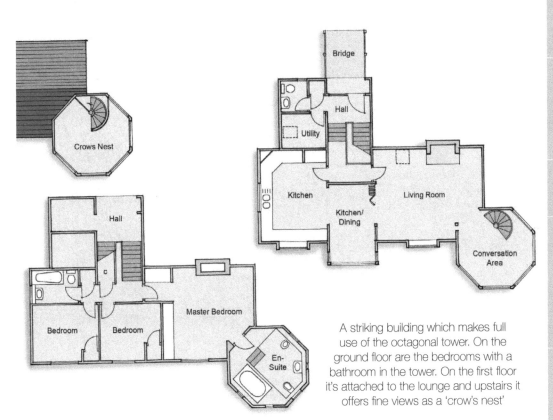

- Bridge
- Hall
- Utility
- Kitchen
- Kitchen/Dining
- Living Room
- Conversation Area
- Crows Nest
- Hall
- c
- Bedroom
- Bedroom
- Master Bedroom
- En-Suite

A striking building which makes full use of the octagonal tower. On the ground floor are the bedrooms with a bathroom in the tower. On the first floor it's attached to the lounge and upstairs it offers fine views as a 'crow's nest'

Contemporary style

Floor area
159m²
1711ft²

Bedrooms
3

Bathrooms
2

Floors
3

Key features
Kitchen/dining room
Utility room
Master en suite
2nd floor 'crow's nest'

Garaging for
0 cars

Design
The Border Design Centre

www.borderdesign.co.uk
borderdesign@btc onnect.com
01578 740218

Build cost
£146,000

Design © The Border Design Centre

Contemporary style

Floor area

160m²

1722ft²

Bedrooms

3

Bathrooms

2

Floors

2

Key features
Basement
Laundry
Living/dining room
Pool in conservatory
Master with sauna

Garaging for
2 cars

Design
**John Shida
(Morningtide
Developments)**

www.morningtide.fsnet.co.uk

johnshida@morningtide.
fsnet.co.uk

01621 815485

Build cost
£147,000

Design © John Shida

Plan no. **BHP 310380**

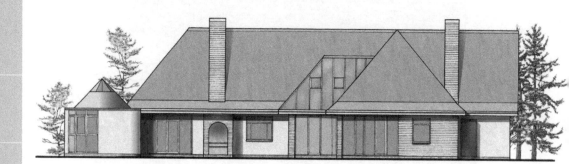

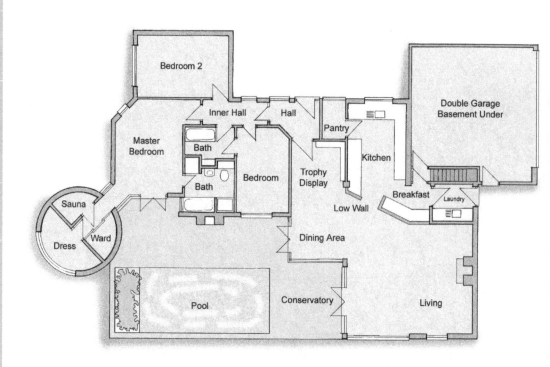

Open-plan living space and three double-sized
bedrooms make this one-storey house a winning
design. There's a sauna in the turreted annexe off the
master bedroom and the option to create a complete
health suite in a basement beneath the garage.

Plan no. **BHP 310374**

Contemporary style

Floor area
162m²
1744ft²

Bedrooms
3

Bathrooms
2

Floors
2

Key features
Basement gym & utility
Kitchen/breakfast area
Swimming pool
Separate dining room
Study

Garaging for
0 cars

Design
Design & Materials

www.designandmaterials.uk.com
enquiries@designandmaterials.uk.com
01909 540 123

Build cost
£149,000

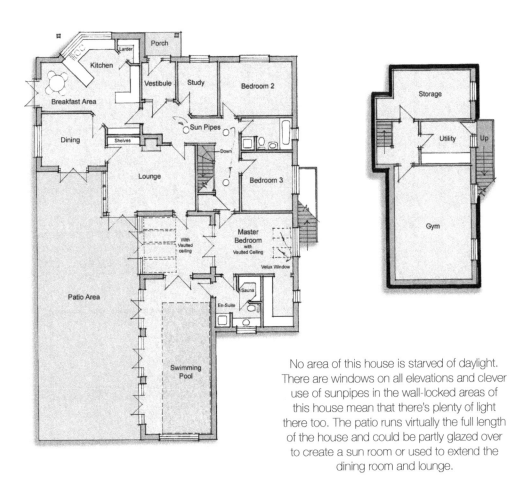

No area of this house is starved of daylight. There are windows on all elevations and clever use of sunpipes in the wall-locked areas of this house mean that there's plenty of light there too. The patio runs virtually the full length of the house and could be partly glazed over to create a sun room or used to extend the dining room and lounge.

Barn style

Floor area
162m²
1744ft²

Bedrooms
3

Bathrooms
2

Floors
2

Key features
Dining hall
Porch
Utility room
Master en suite
Study area

Garaging for
0 cars

Design
Potton

www.potton.co.uk
contact@potton.co.uk
01767 676 400

Build cost
£149,000

Plan no. **BHP 310782**

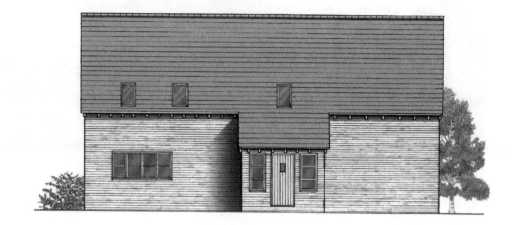

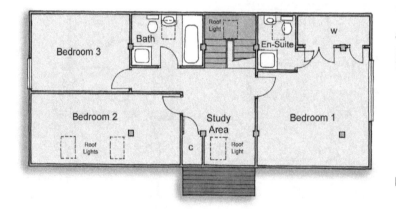

This is a great design for areas where overlooking objections could cause a problem. The rooflights provide the light but their flush fit means they can't be used for gawping at neighbours. Inside, a porch gives on to a grand dining hall with a lounge and kitchen off either side. Upstairs the three bedrooms are all large and the master has the ubiquitous en-suite facilities.

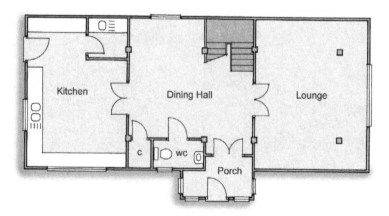

Plan no. **BHP 310512**

Breakfast/Dining

Terrace

Sitting Room

Kitchen

Utility

Entrance Hall

c

c

Music Room

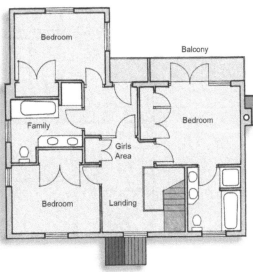

Bedroom

Balcony

Family

Girls Area

Bedroom

Bedroom

Landing

The ground floor of this design is effectively open plan and makes brilliant use of the space available. Upstairs a two-way balcony and two large bathrooms add luxury while built-in storage adds practicality.

Traditional style

Floor area
162m²
1744ft²

Bedrooms
3

Bathrooms
2

Floors
2

Key features
Kitchen/breakfast room
Utility room
Music room
Master en suite

Garaging for
0 cars

Design
Stephen Mattick

www.mattick.co.uk
mattick@mattick.co.uk
01223 891159

Build cost
£149,000

Traditional style

Floor area
165m²
1776ft²

Bedrooms
3

Bathrooms
3

Floors
1

Key features
Separate dining room
Utility room
Study
Master en suite

Garaging for
0 cars

Design
Custom Homes

www.customhomes.co.uk
admin@customhomes.co.uk
01787 377388

Build cost
£151,000

Design © Custom Homes

Plan no. **BHP 310419**

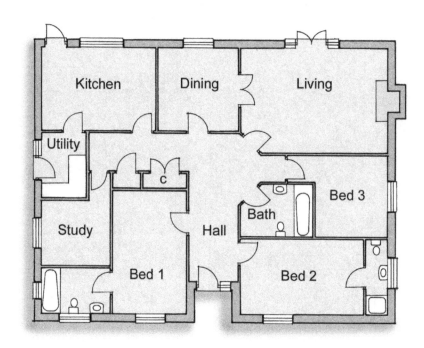

Single-storey houses don't have to be cramped as this double-fronted design proves. If height issues are a problem on your site or you like the idea of stairless living then this could be the home for you.

Plan no. **BHP 310626**

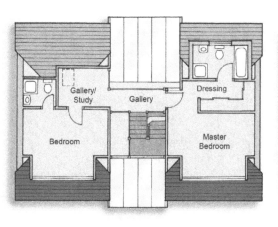

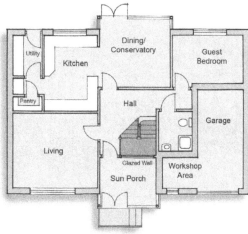

Thirties-style dormers peak out of the roof of this design and blend perfectly with the modern full-height glass frontage. There's a matching glass elevation at the rear so the main ground floor rooms are bathed in daylight. The first floor has a gallery landing and a pair of en-suite bedrooms.

Contemporary style

Floor area
166m²
1787ft²

Bedrooms
3

Bathrooms
3

Floors
2

Key features
Dining/conservatory
Sun porch
Utility room
Pantry
Master en suite

Garaging for
1 car

Design
**The Bespoke
Design Company**

www.planahome.uk.com
plans@planahome.uk.com
01326 373600

Build cost
£152,500

Traditional style

Floor area
168m²
1808ft²

Bedrooms
3

Bathrooms
2

Floors
2

Key features
Kitchen/dining room
Conservatory
Utility room
Porch
Master en suite

Garaging for
0 cars

Design
Welsh Oak Frame

www.welshoakframe.com
01686 688000

Build cost
£154,500

Design © Welsh Oak Frame

Plan no. **BHP 310548**

The oak framed-heart of this house is worn on its part-timbered front elevation. nside an expansive kitchen leads into an equally large dining room and conservatory. Extending the conservatory across the back of the house would connect all the living spaces for perfect flow between rooms.

Plan no. **BHP 310431**

Take a look at the clever touches in this design and you can imagine yourself living in it. There's the utility room that leads off the garage – great for cleaning up after a morning under the bonnet or in the garden. The kitchen has a glass roof so it's a light and uplifting place to be. Upstairs each bedroom has built in wardrobes and the store in bedroom two could become a second en-suite bathroom.

Traditional style

Floor area
168m²
1808ft²

Bedrooms
3

Bathrooms
2

Floors
2

Key features
Kitchen/breakfast room
Utility room
Study/dining room
Master en suite

Garaging for
1 car

Design
Stephen Mattick

www.mattick.co.uk
mattick@mattick.co.uk
01223 891159

Build cost
£154,500

Design © Stephen Mattick

Contemporary style

Floor area
168m²
1808ft²

Bedrooms
3

Bathrooms
2

Floors
2

Key features
Kitchen/diner
Utility room
Workshop
Dressing room

Garaging for
1 car

Design
Potton

www.potton.co.uk
contact@potton.co.uk
01767 676 400

Build cost
£154,500

Design © Potton

Plan no. **BHP 310218**

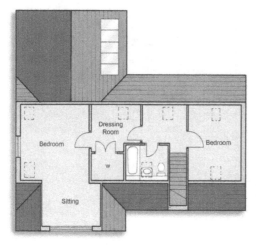

Don't let the low roofline fool you. This design features two storeys of living and sleeping space. The large kitchen is well lit by windows on three sides and from above via rooflights. There's also potential for two reception rooms accessed off the wide hall. Upstairs the impressive master suite gets lots of natural light thanks to the gable window and twin rooflights.

Plan no. **BHP 310908**

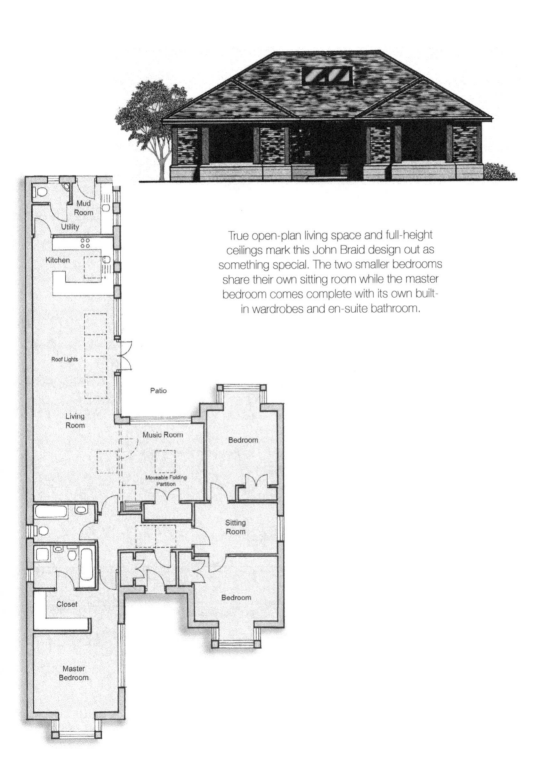

True open-plan living space and full-height ceilings mark this John Braid design out as something special. The two smaller bedrooms share their own sitting room while the master bedroom comes complete with its own built-in wardrobes and en-suite bathroom.

Traditional style

Floor area
173m²
1862ft²

Bedrooms
3

Bathrooms
2

Floors
1

Key features
Open-plan living space
Music room
Sitting room
Utility/mud room
Master en suite

Garaging for
0 cars

Design
John Braid
(at Leslie R Hutt)

lhuttarchitect@btinternet.com
01463 235566

Build cost
£160,000

Traditional style

Floor area
175m²
1884ft²

Bedrooms
3

Bathrooms
2

Floors
3

Key features
Staircase in turret
Utility room
Study
Master en suite

Garaging for
2 cars

Design
The Border Design
Centre

www.borderdesign.co.uk
borderdesign@btconnect.com
01578 740218

Build cost
£161,000

Plan no. **BHP 310974**

You can make the best possible use of a building plot by building down as well as up as this design shows. Your cars and your washing are kept below stairs leaving two further floors for an open-plan living area, study and three bedrooms.

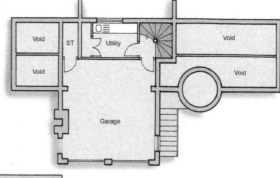

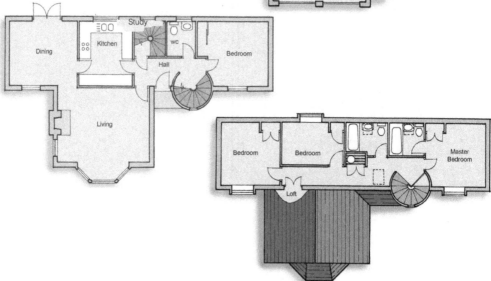

Plan no. **BHP 310341**

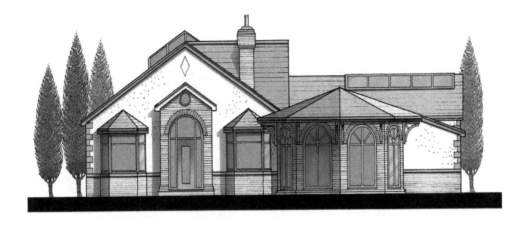

Light is a major feature of this house, it floods in everywhere thanks to acres of glazing. A vast indoor swimming pool and an underground leisure suite are both desirable luxury assets.

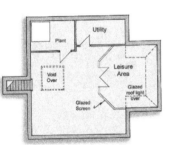

Traditional style

Floor area
177m²
1905ft²

Bedrooms
3

Bathrooms
2

Floors
2

Key features
Swimming pool
Kitchen/breakfast room
Basement leisure area
Conservatory
Dining room

Garaging for
0 cars

Design
James Campbell Associates

01706 354888

Build cost
£163,000

Traditional style

Floor area
180m²
1938ft²

Bedrooms
3

Bathrooms
3

Floors
2

Key features
Kitchen/dining room
Master en suite
Utility room

Garaging for
0 cars

Design
**Taylor & Co
Architects**

www.taylorandcoarchitects.co.uk
design@taylorandcoarchitects.co.uk
01905 621600

Build cost
£165,500

Design © Taylor & Co
Architects

Plan no. **BHP 310653**

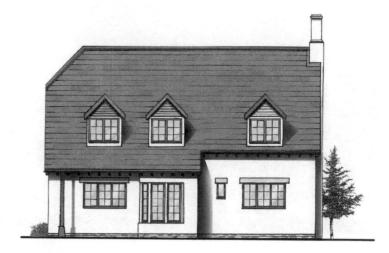

This design gives cottage looks but has acres of space inside. The kitchen and living room are positioned at right angles to each other predicting the likely flow between the two spaces. The master suite takes a dominant, full-depth position upstairs. But those in the other bedrooms shouldn't feel too envious because both are generous doubles with space for an en-suite apiece.

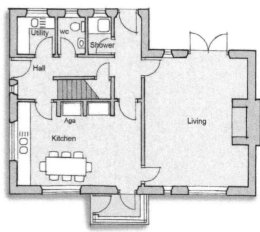

Plan no. **BHP 310281**

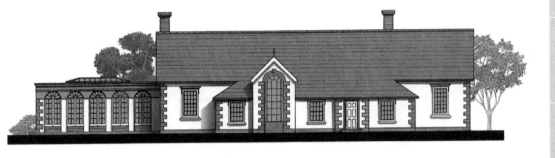

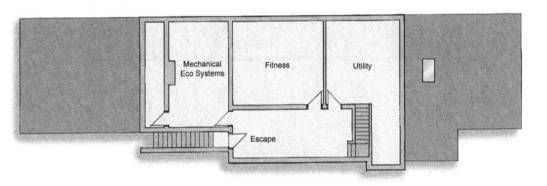

Mechanical Eco Systems — Fitness — Utility — Escape

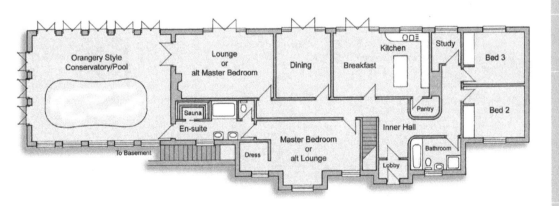

Orangery Style Conservatory/Pool — Lounge or alt Master Bedroom — Dining — Breakfast — Kitchen — Study — Bed 3 — Sauna — En-suite — To Basement — Dress — Master Bedroom or alt Lounge — Lobby — Inner Hall — Pantry — Bed 2 — Bathroom

Traditional style

Floor area
183m²
1970ft²

Bedrooms
3

Bathrooms
2

Floors
2

Key features
Indoor pool

Garaging for
0 cars

Design
Jeremy Rawlings

www.periodhome.net
01884 266444

Build cost
£168,000

High ceilings make this single storey house feel extremely spacious and the well-thought-out layout adds to this impression. A large indoor pool leads on from the optional master bedroom or lounge. Downstairs in the basement there's a gym and a large utility room.

Traditional style

Floor area
191m²
2056ft²

Bedrooms
3

Bathrooms
2

Floors
2

Key features
Triple aspect family room

Garaging for
0 cars

Design
Opus Architecture and Design

01252 861759

Build cost
£176,000

Plan no. **BHP 311001**

You'll feel immediately at home in this design with its hallway-based open fire. Beyond the fire a dining hall and a roof lit, triple aspect, family room offers further comfort after a tough day at work. There's a first floor lounge with a balcony to take advantage of a great view. The first floor also includes a study and a large master suite.

Plan no. **BHP 310473**

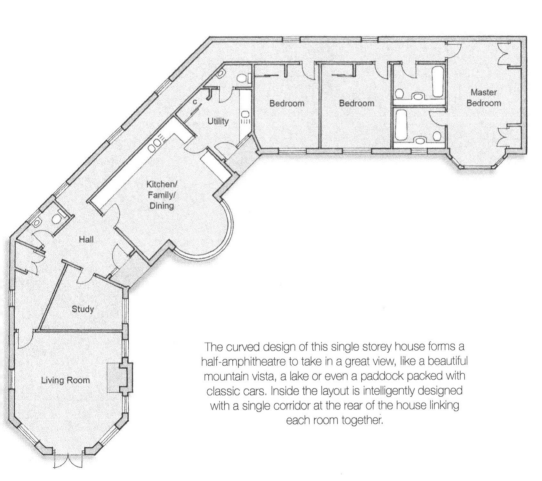

Utility

Bedroom

Bedroom

Master Bedroom

Kitchen/ Family/ Dining

Hall

Study

Living Room

The curved design of this single storey house forms a half-amphitheatre to take in a great view, like a beautiful mountain vista, a lake or even a paddock packed with classic cars. Inside the layout is intelligently designed with a single corridor at the rear of the house linking each room together.

Traditional style

Floor area
191m²
2056ft²

Bedrooms
3

Bathrooms
2

Floors
1

Key features
Kitchen/family room
Living room
Study
Utility
Master en suite

Garaging for
0 cars

Design
The Border Design Centre

www.borderdesign.co.uk
borderdesign@btconnect.com
01578 740218

Build cost
£176,000

Design © Border Design Centre

Traditional style

Floor area
193m²
2077ft²

Bedrooms
3

Bathrooms
2

Floors
2

Key features
Vaulted lounge
Kitchen/diner
Music room
Utility room
Art studio

Garaging for
0 cars

Design
Potton

www.potton.co.uk
contact@potton.co.uk
01767 676 400

Build cost
£177,500

Design © Potton

Plan no. **BHP 310575**

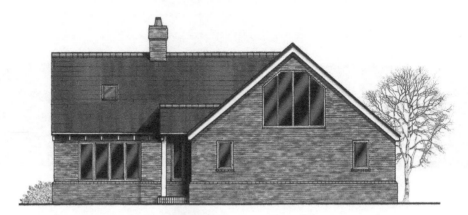

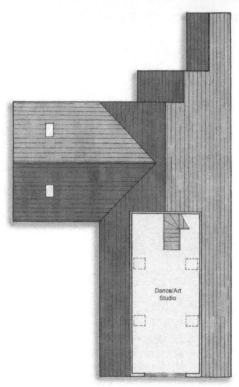

The spacious hall provides a welcoming entrance to this home with natural light coming from the front door, side windows and internal glazed doors. The lounge ceiling is vaulted and is lit by windows on both sides and two above. The single first floor room runs for more than half the length of the house and would make an excellent office, studio or self-contained guest suite.

Plan no. **BHP 310203**

Contemporary style

Balcony

Balcony

Vaulted
Ceiling

Master
Bedroom

Breakfast

Dressing

Kitchen

Hall/Lobby

Combining the kitchen, breakfast and living room under a vaulted ceiling makes the first floor of this design seem exceptionally spacious. Downstairs two bedrooms and a family room spread out in plenty of space.

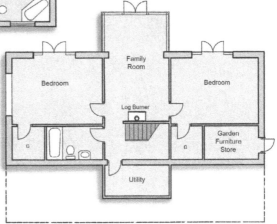

Family
Room

Bedroom

Bedroom

Log Burner

Garden
Furniture
Store

Utility

Floor area
195m²
2099ft²

Bedrooms
3

Bathrooms
2

Floors
2

Key features
Upside-down living
Open plan living area
Balconies
Family room
Master en suite

Garaging for
0 cars

Design
Chaddock Design

www.dreamspelldesign.co.uk
info@dreamspelldesign.
co.uk
01789 459148

Build cost
£179,000

Floor area
200m²
2153ft²

Bedrooms
3

Bathrooms
2

Floors
2

Key features
Observation tower
Separate dining room
Utility room
Galleried landing
Master en suite

Garaging for
1 car

Design
**The Border Design
Centre**

www.borderdesign.co.uk
borderdesign@btconnect.com
01578 740218

Build cost
£184,000

Plan no. **BHP 310980**

You can take advantage of a great view with this design's built-in observation tower and multi-windowed garden annexe. Bed and living rooms are spread between ground and first floors to make the best use of the available space.

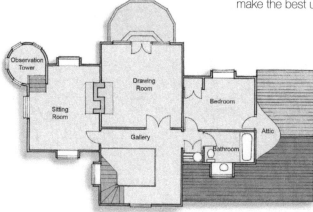

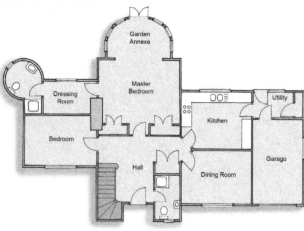

Plan no. **BHP 310596**

The weatherboard finish gives this house true country credentials but that doesn't mean you have to put up with straw-covered floors and livestock inside. What you get is a great open space downstairs, double-sized bedrooms upstairs plus lots of extra storage room in the eaves.

Traditional style

Floor area
200m²
2153ft²

Bedrooms
3

Bathrooms
3

Floors
2

Key features
Kitchen/dining room
Utility room
Study
Master en suite
Dressing room

Garaging for
1 car

Design
Border Oak

www.borderoak.com
sales@borderoak.com
01568 708752

Build cost
£184,000

Design © Border Oak

Contemporary style

Floor area
200m²
2153ft²

Bedrooms
3

Bathrooms
2

Floors
3

Key features
Vaulted ceilings

Garaging for
0 cars

Design
Design & Materials

www.designandmaterials.uk.com
enquiries@designandmaterials.uk.com
01909 540 123

Build cost
£184,000

Plan no. **BHP 310572**

The spacious entrance hall in this house is designed to have lots of natural light thanks to strategically placed rooflights in the roof. The main living areas flow neatly into each other through fold back doors and all have access to a large balcony. The attic space offers space for an extra bedroom, study or playroom and there's also some handy extra storage in the eaves.

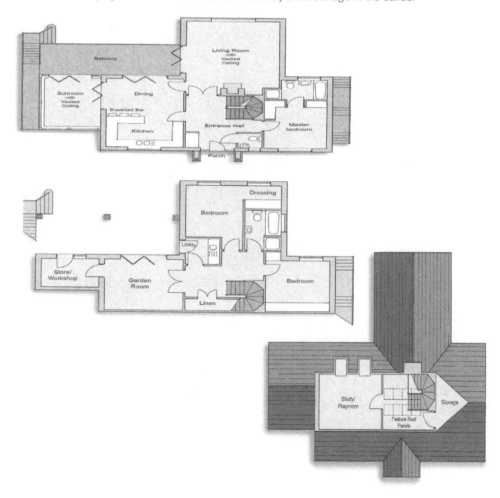

Plan no. **BHP 310563**

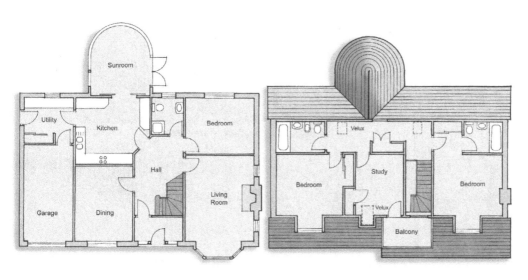

Floor area
204m²
2196ft²

Bedrooms
3

Bathrooms
3

Floors
2

Key features
Sun room
Separate dining room
Utility room
Study
Master en suite

Garaging for
1 car

Design
The Border Design Centre

www.borderdesign.co.uk
borderdesign@btconnect.com
01578 740218

Build cost
£187,500

The semi-circular sun room in this The Border Design Centre house would
be a great place to look over a cherished garden while you pick through
your morning museli. Other great touches in this house include a first floor
balcony and twin upstairs bed and bathrooms.

Traditional style

Floor area
205m²
2207ft²

Bedrooms
3

Bathrooms
3

Floors
2

Key features
Kitchen/diner
Utility room
StudyMaster en suite
Dressing room

Garaging for
1 car

Design
Border Oak

www.borderoak.com
sales@borderoak.com
01568 708752

Build cost
£188,500

Design © Border Oak

Plan no. **BHP 310752**

This house has plenty of open-plan spaces on the ground floor, three big bedrooms on the first floor and some useful storage spaces built into the roof void too. Finished in wood cladding the house would blend in well in a rural environment but switch materials and you could slot it just about anywhere.

Plan no. **BHP 310497**

Traditional style

Floor area
205m²
2207ft²

Bedrooms
3

Bathrooms
2

Floors
2

The first floor sitting room and balcony in this design is perfect to take advantage of a beautiful view. Across the landing the master bedroom has a generous en-suite bathroom built into the eaves. Downstairs an expansive hall leads onto two more bedrooms and a large kitchen with utility and cloakrooms attached.

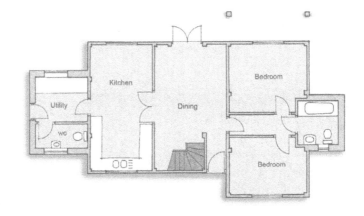

Key features
Large kitchen
Dining hall
Utility room
Study
Master en suite

Garaging for
0 cars

Design
**TJ Crump
Oakwrights**

www.oakwrights.co.uk
enquiries@oakwrights.co.uk
01432 353353

Build cost
£188,500

Design © TJ Crump

Traditional style

Floor area
205m²
2207ft²

Bedrooms
3

Bathrooms
3

Floors
2

Key features
Sun room
Utility room
Separate dining room
Master en suite

Garaging for
0 cars

Design
Border Oak

www.borderoak.com
sales@borderoak.com
01568 708752

Build cost
£188,500

Design © Border Oak

Plan no. **BHP 310134**

Behind the classic exterior of this Border Oak house are all the accoutrements of modern living including a double-glazed sun room, big kitchen, dining, and sitting rooms. The first floor features three bedrooms with a full-width master suite complete with dressing room and bathroom.

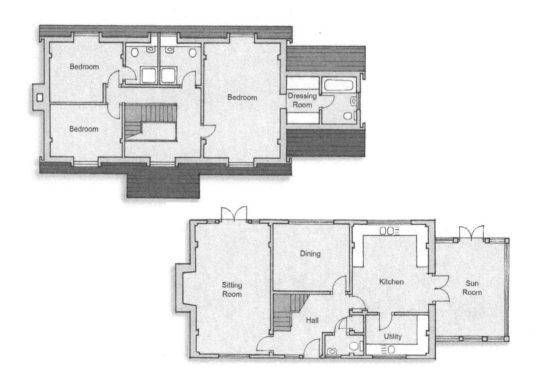

Plan no. **BHP 310476**

The decorated eaves and mullioned windows give this John Braid design a classic look from the outside. To keep the front uncluttered there's an entrance porch at the side of the house leading into a large entrance hall that flows to all the ground floor living spaces. It would be easy to create a feature kitchen by making it open plan with the dining room and fitting folding/sliding doors to the veranda.

Traditional style

Floor area
211m²
2271ft²

Bedrooms
3

Bathrooms
2

Floors
2

Key features
Porch
Galleried hall/landing
Utility room
Master en suite
Veranda

Garaging for
0 cars

Design
**John Braid
(at Leslie R Hutt)**

lhuttarchitect@btinternet.com
01463 235566

Build cost
£194,000

Design © Leslie R Hutt

Traditional style

Floor area
213m²
2293ft²

Bedrooms
3

Bathrooms
3

Floors
2

Key features
Kitchen/breakfast room
Study
Utility room
Master en suite

Garaging for
1 car

Design
Churchill Design

www.churchilldesign.co.uk
info@churchilldesign.co.uk
01252 325701

Build cost
£196,000

Design © Churchill Design

Plan no. **BHP 310212**

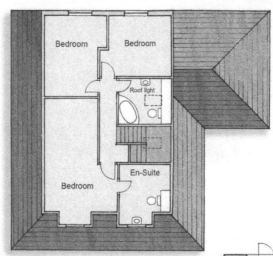

Despite a low roof height this house fits in three bedrooms easily by using dormer windows and rooflights to provide extra headroom and light upstairs. The living room, with its twin-aspect windows, could be linked with the kitchen/breakfast room by building a conservatory across the back of the house.

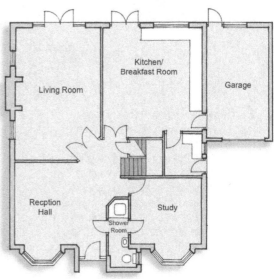

Plan no. **BHP 310014**

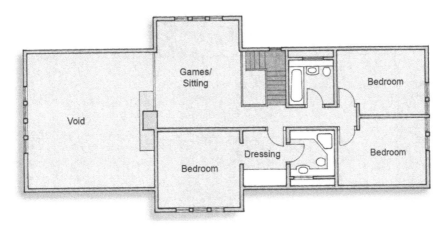

Games/Sitting

Void

Bedroom

Bedroom

Dressing

Bedroom

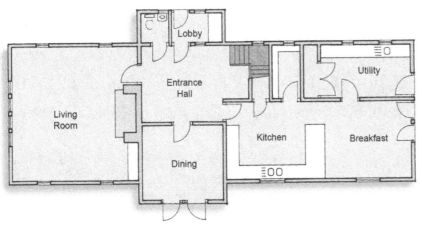

Lobby

Entrance Hall

Utility

Living Room

Kitchen

Breakfast

Dining

A double-height living room in this barn-style house creates an impressive space to entertain in. On the first floor a games/sitting room overlooks the living room through a glazed panel. Using balustrades instead of glass for this division would make a superb, open gallery feature.

Barn style

Floor area

214m²

2303ft²

Bedrooms

3

Bathrooms

2

Floors

2

Key features
Kitchen/breakfast room
Separate dining room
Utility room
Double height lounge
Games room

Garaging for
0 cars

Design
Welsh Oak Frame

www.welshoakframe.com
01686 688000

Build cost
£197,000

Design © Welsh Oak Frame

Contemporary style

Floor area
220m²
2368ft²

Bedrooms
3

Bathrooms
1

Floors
2

Key features
Big entrance hall
Study
Utility room

Garaging for
1 car

Design
Churchill Design

www.churchilldesign.co.uk
info@churchilldesign.co.uk
01252 325701

Build cost
£202,500

Design © Churchill Design

Plan no. **BHP 310812**

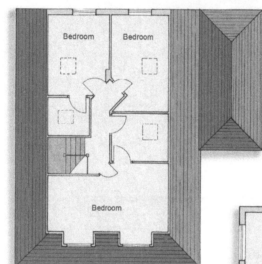

This is a smart low roofline design whose dormer windows allow bedrooms and bathrooms to be built into the eaves. Downstairs the entrance hall is cavernous and could easily accommodate a dining table, while the kitchen and living room both have direct access to the garden through French doors.

Plan no. **BHP 310269**

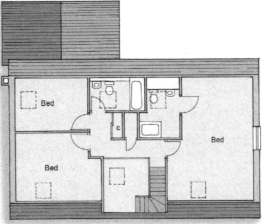

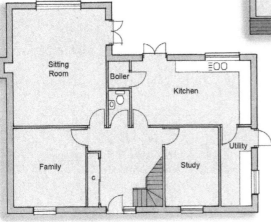

Good old Velux-type windows come in handy when you've got issues with overlooking on your building plot. This design makes great use of them and allows three bedrooms into the wide first floor area. Downstairs there are two reception rooms and the potential for a vaulted ceiling detail over one end of the sitting room.

Traditional style

Floor area
223m²
2400ft²

Bedrooms
3

Bathrooms
2

Floors
2

Key features
Kitchen/breakfast room
Family room
Study
Utility room
Master en suite

Garaging for
0 cars

Design
Custom Homes

www.customhomes.co.uk
admin@customhomes.co.uk
01787 377388

Build cost
£200,000

Design © Custom Homes

Contemporary style

Floor area
225m²
2422ft²

Bedrooms
3

Bathrooms
2

Floors
3

Key features
Three storeys
Kitchen/dining room
Study
Playroom
Master en suite

Garaging for
0 cars

Design
Richard Hall

07968 407129

Build cost
£202,000

Design © Richard Hall

Plan no. **BHP 310704**

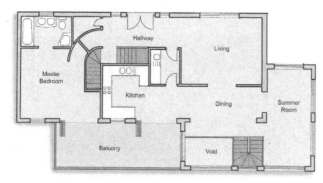

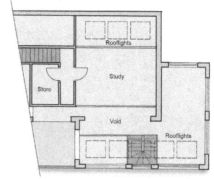

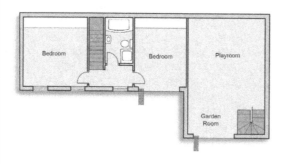

This futuristic design makes maximum use of the available space with its open-plan rooms and three-level layout. The ground floor takes in all the available sunlight with its mass of glazing and full-height folding/sliding doors.

Plan no. **BHP 310260**

From the outside this looks a lot like a single storey house but thanks to flush-fitting rooflights there's a decent-sized first floor on offer. This design will work well in areas where planning for a conventional two-storey house wouldn't be permitted because of overlooking concerns with adjacent properties.

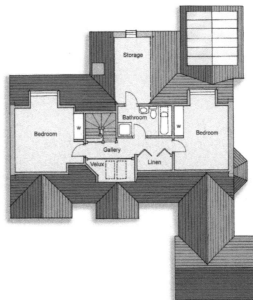

Traditional style

Floor area
230m²
2476ft²

Bedrooms
3

Bathrooms
2

Floors
2

Key features
Kitchen/breakfast room
Study
Utility room
Sun room
Separate dining room

Garaging for
1 cars

Design
Design & Materials

www.designandmaterials.uk.com
enquiries@designandmaterials.uk.com
01909 540 123

£

Build cost
£206,000

Design © Design & Materials

Contemporary style

Floor area
230m²
2476ft²

Bedrooms
3

Bathrooms
3

Floors
2

Key features
Kitchen/Breakfast room
Utility room
Study
Sun lounge
Master en suite

Garaging for
0 car

Design
**John Braid
(at Leslie R Hutt)**

lhuttarchitect@btinternet.com
01463 235566

Build cost
£206,000

Design © Leslie R Hutt

Plan no. **BHP 310863**

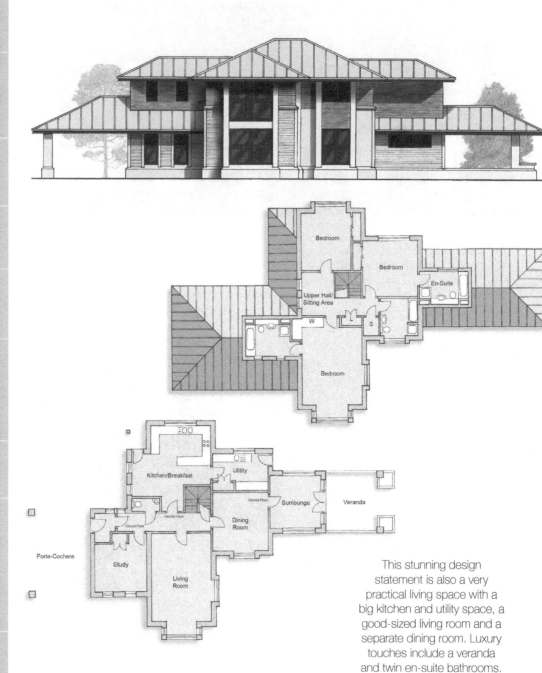

This stunning design statement is also a very practical living space with a big kitchen and utility space, a good-sized living room and a separate dining room. Luxury touches include a veranda and twin en-suite bathrooms.

Plan no. **BHP 310941**

Where an uneven site causes building problems this stilt design could save the day. The basement area created by the raised 'ground floor' houses a garage, above which sits the master bedroom and a spare reception room. The bay-fronted conservatory creates a great feature at the end of a kitchen that also includes dining space and twin aspect windows. Upstairs the first floor features two large bedrooms and a family bathroom.

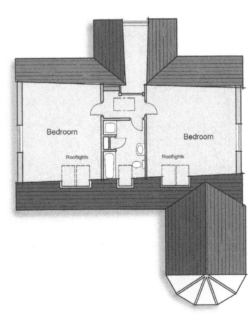

Contemporary style

Floor area
233m²
2508ft²

Bedrooms
3

Bathrooms
2

Floors
3

Key features
Kitchen/breakfast area
Conservatory
Master en suite
Study
Utility room

Garaging for
2 cars

Design
JS Building Consultancy

www.ukbuildingconsultancy.co.uk
jsharples@ricsonline.org
0113 250 1303

Build cost
£209,000

Design © JS Building Consultancy

Traditional style

Floor area
235m²
2530ft²

Bedrooms
3

Bathrooms
3

Floors
2

Key features
Porch
Separate dining room
Family room
Utility room
3 en suites

Garaging for
2 cars

Design
Border Oak

www.borderoak.com
sales@borderoak.com
01568 708752

Build cost
£211,000

Design © Border Oak

Plan no. **BHP 310071**

A terrific blend of building materials from thatch through to wooden cladding gives this house a country cottage feel. But the accommodation on offer from the L-shaped layout is a world away from the traditional cramped cottage. The pitch roof over the garage and kitchen could become an office, a fourth bedroom or a self-contained guest suite.

Plan no. **BHP 310584**

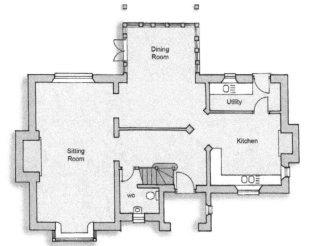

The trad-look front of this house hides a fully modern open-plan ground floor living space. Upstairs a large landing leads on to three bedrooms. All the bedrooms are large so it would be simple enough to slot an extra room in if necessary.

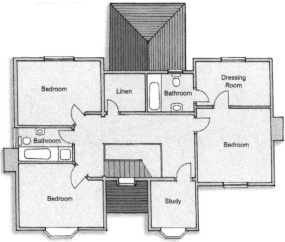

Traditional style

Floor area
240m²
2583ft²

Bedrooms
3

Bathrooms
2

Floors
2

Key features
Dining room
Galleried landing
Master en suite
Dressing room

Garaging for
0 cars

Design
**TJ Crump
Oakwrights**

www.oakwrights.co.uk
enquiries@oakwrights.co.uk
01432 353353

Build cost
£215,000

Design © TJ Crump
Oakwrights

Barn style

Floor area
260m²
2799ft²

Bedrooms
3

Bathrooms
4

Floors
2

Key features
Vaulted living space
Open-plan layout
Sauna
Utility room
En-suite master bed

Garaging for
0 cars

Design
Design & Materials

www.designandmaterials.uk.com
enquiries@designandmaterials.
uk.com
01909 540 123

Build cost
£233,000

Design © Design &
Materials

Plan no. **BHP 310518**

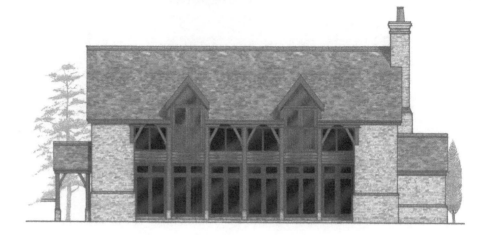

A completely open-plan living area for those who
require maximum flexibility. Features include the
ground floor sauna and a master bedroom suite with
its own bathroom on a mezzanine level.

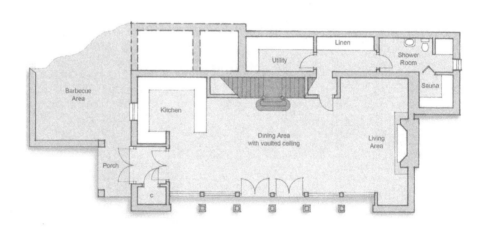

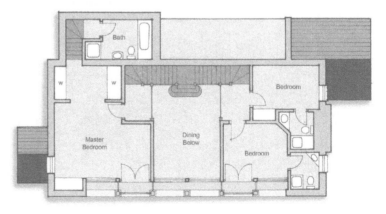

Plan no. **BHP 310860**

The ground floor features well laid out living space including an integral kitchen and breakfast room while the link through to the garage contains a utility room. There are three more reception rooms downstairs and three bedrooms and en-suite bathrooms upstairs.

Contemporary style

Floor area
260m²
2799ft²

Bedrooms
3

Bathrooms
3

Floors
2

Key features
Kitchen/breakfast room
Family room
Study
Dining room
Utility room

Garaging for
2 cars

Design
John Braid
(at Leslie R Hutt)

lhuttarchitect@btinternet.com
01463 235566

Build cost
£233,000

Design © John Braid

Traditional style

Floor area
270m²
2906ft²

Bedrooms
3

Bathrooms
3

Floors
2

Key features
Family room
Dining room
Galleried landing
Study

Garaging for
0 cars

Design
Border Oak

www.borderoak.com
sales@borderoak.com
01568 708752

Build cost
£242,000

The fully-glazed two-storey bay lights a double-height hallway that leads into an open-plan dining room and kitchen. Off the family room a second staircase leads up to a useful space above the garage – a perfect spot for a gym or home office.

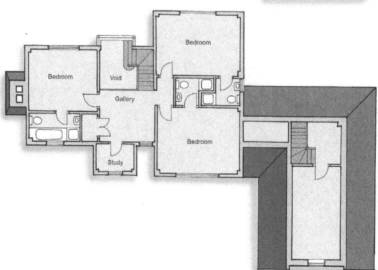

Plan no. **BHP** 310167

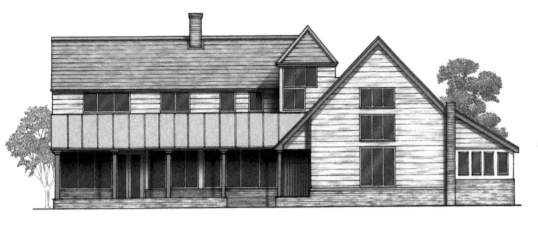

The veranda acts as an additional link between the main reception rooms. Upstairs are three good-sized bedrooms with a dressing room and en-suite bathroom for the master.

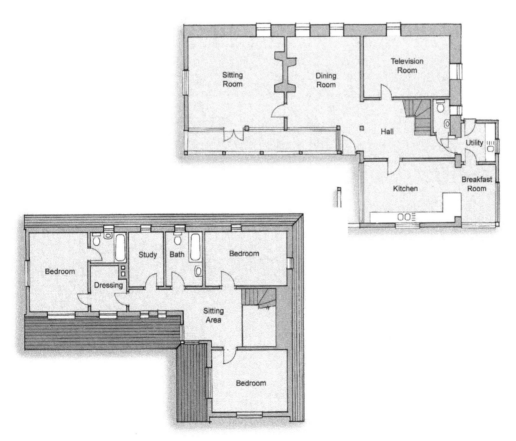

Traditional style

Floor area
291m²
3132ft²

Bedrooms
3

Bathrooms
2

Floors
2

Key features
Kitchen/breakfast room
Television room
Study
Master bed en-suite
Dressing room

Garaging for
0 cars

Design
Border Oak

www.borderoak.com
sales@borderoak.com
01568 708752

Build cost
£261,000

Design © Border Oak

Barn style

Floor area

342m²

3681ft²

Bedrooms

3

Bathrooms

3

Floors

2

Key Features
Courtyard
Kitchen/breakfast room
Study
Dining/sitting room
Master en-suite

Garaging for
0 cars

Design
Stephen Mattick

www.mattick.co.uk
mattick@mattick.co.uk
01223 891159

Build cost
£307,000

Design © S Mattick

Plan no. **BHP 310593**

The twin single-storey sections of this house form an impressive courtyard entrance that can be seen from the kitchen, study and one of the three bedrooms. Inside, the glass-roofed hallway leads into a dining room and a double-height sitting room. The entire first floor is given over to a sleeping suite equipped with a dressing room and its own bathroom.

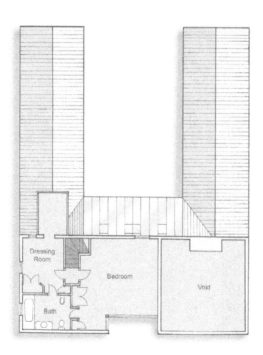

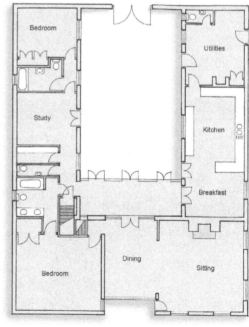

Plan no. **BHP** **310959**

Strongly ornamented chimneys, rendered walls and exposed rafter feet give this design a period look. Inside the main reception rooms all offer plenty of space.

Traditional style

Floor area
353m²
3800ft²

Bedrooms
3

Bathrooms
3

Floors
2

Exceptional Features
Integral garage
Utility room
Master en-suite

Garaging for
2 cars

Design
Border Oak

www.borderoak.com
sales@borderoak.com
01568 708752

Build cost
£316,500

Design © Border Oak

Contemporary style

Floor area

353m²

3800ft²

Bedrooms

3

Bathrooms

3

Floors

3

Key features
Open-plan living
TV room
Bedroom balconies
Gym
Swimming pool

Garaging for
cars

Design
Design & Materials

www.designandmaterials.uk.com
enquiries@designandmaterials.
uk.com
01909 540 123

Build cost
£316,500

Design © Design and
Materials

Plan no. **BHP 310608**

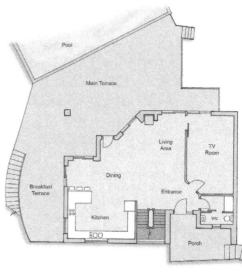

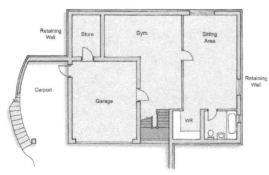

This house featres a downstairs gym
and a poolside terrace that leads
into an open-plan living area. A vast
double-height window lights the
stairwell up to the first floor sleeping
quarters where all the bedrooms have
their own balconies.

Plan no. **BHP 310707**

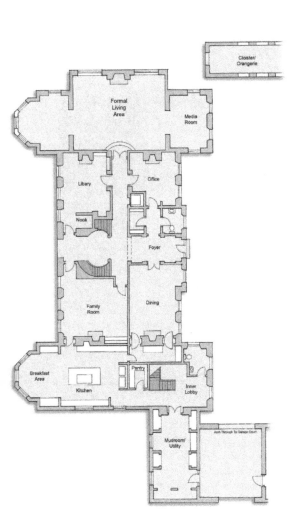

This Georgian-style mansion is packed with features. It offers a fitness suite, home theatre but just three bedrooms. However, it would be easy to change this design to offer more bedrooms and fewer reception rooms.

Traditional style

Floor area
371m²
3993ft²

Bedrooms
3

Bathrooms
5

Floors
2

Key features
Home theatre
Sauna
Jacuzzi room
Library
Orangery

Garaging for
0 cars

Design
Angel Design and Development

01788 573676

Build cost
£333,000

Design © Angel Design and Development

Barn style

Floor area
585m²
6297ft²

Bedrooms
3

Bathrooms
3

Floors
2

Key features
Office
Separate dining room
Mud room
Bedrooms en-suite
Two staircases

Garaging for
2 cars

Design
TJ Crump
Oakwrights

www.oakwrights.co.uk
enquiries@oakwrights.co.uk
01432 353353

Build cost
£525,000

Plan no. **BHP 310803**

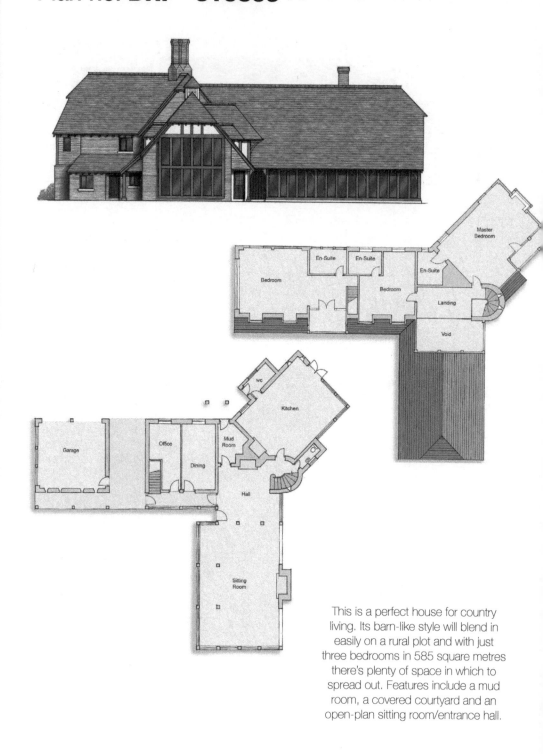

This is a perfect house for country living. Its barn-like style will blend in easily on a rural plot and with just three bedrooms in 585 square metres there's plenty of space in which to spread out. Features include a mud room, a covered courtyard and an open-plan sitting room/entrance hall.

Plan no. **BHP 310686**

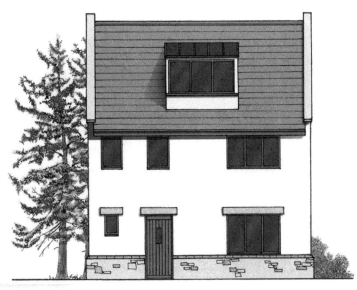

Traditional style

Floor area
106m²
1141ft²

Bedrooms
4

Bathrooms
1

Floors
3

Key features
Living/dining room
Attic bedroom

Garaging for
0 cars

Design
Architecture Plus

www.architecture-plus.co.uk
01934 416416

£

Build cost
£110,000

Design © Architecture Plus

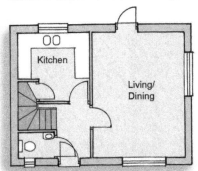

This design's dormer window creates space and light for an extra bedroom in a house with a very small footprint. The ground floor provides a living/ dining area.

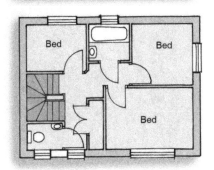

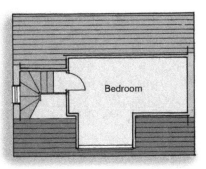

Traditional style

Floor area
114m²
1227ft²

Bedrooms
4

Bathrooms
2

Floors
3

Key features
Kitchen/dining room
Top floor suite

Garaging for
1 car

Design
Planahome

www.planahome.uk.com
plans@planahome.uk.com
01326 373600

Build cost
£119,000

Design © Planahome

Plan no. **BHP 310764**

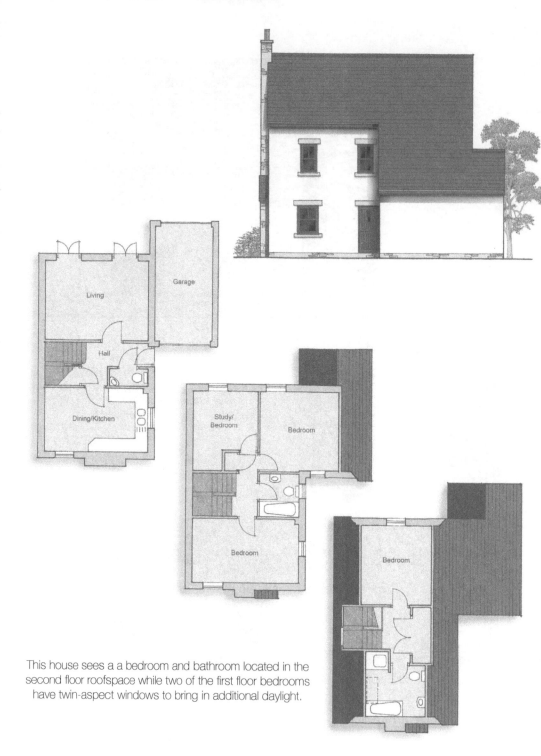

This house sees a a bedroom and bathroom located in the second floor roofspace while two of the first floor bedrooms have twin-aspect windows to bring in additional daylight.

Plan no. **BHP 310965**

Four bedrooms are fitted into the first floor of this compact home. The living room features a conservatory which adds to the flexibility and helps create a sheltered terrace.

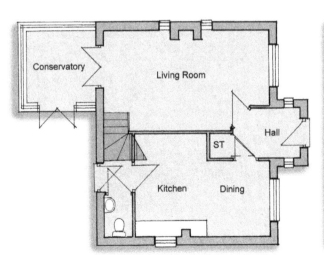

Conservatory

Living Room

ST

Hall

Kitchen

Dining

Bedroom 3

Bedroom 2

ST

ST

Bedroom 4

Bedroom 1

Traditional style

Floor area
121m²
1302ft²

Bedrooms
4

Bathrooms
2

Floors
2

Key features
Conservatory
Kitchen/dining room
Hall
Master en-suite

Garaging for
0 cars

Design
Architecture Plus

www.architecture-plus.co.uk
01934 416416

Build cost
£126,000

Design © Architecture Plus

Traditional style

Floor area
122m²
1313ft²

Bedrooms
4

Bathrooms
2

Floors
2

Key features
Kitchen/beakfast room
Utility room
Separate dining room
Master bed en-suite

Garaging for
1 car

Design
Planahome

www.planahome.uk.com
plans@planahome.uk.com
01326 373600

Build cost
£128,000

Design © Planahome

Plan no. **BHP 310275**

A four-bed family home with a kitchen/breakfast room and a lounge/dining room which can be separated by closing the interconnecting double doors.

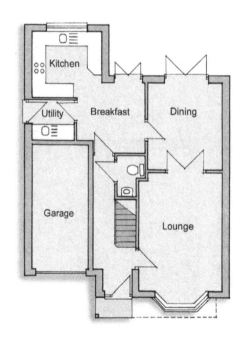

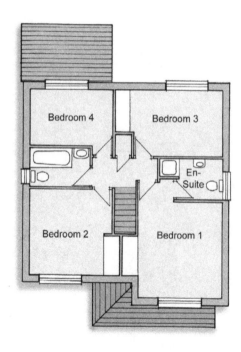

Plan no. **BHP 310899**

The three floors here will make the best of a narrow plot. On the second floor is a master bedroom with en-suite and the first floor has a further three bedrooms and a bathroom.

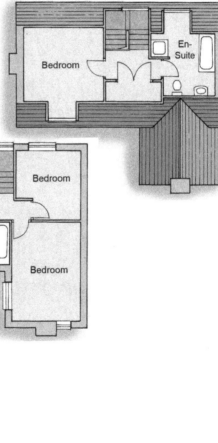

Bedroom

En-Suite

Bedroom

Bedroom

Bedroom

Bath

Bedroom

Lounge

ST

Dining

Utility

WC

Kitchen

Traditional style

Floor area
122m²
1313ft²

Bedrooms
4

Bathrooms
2

Floors
3

Key features
Top floor suite
Utility room
Separate dining room

Garaging for
0 cars

Design
Planahome

www.planahome.uk.com
plans@planahome.uk.com
01326 373600

Build cost
£128,000

Design © Planahome

Traditional style

Floor area
124m²
1335ft²

Bedrooms
4

Bathrooms
2

Floors
2

Key features
Utility room
Separate dining room
Master bed en-suite

Garaging for
car

Design
Planahome

www.planahome.uk.com
plans@planahome.uk.com
01326 373600

Build cost
£129,000

Design © Planahome

Plan no. **BHP 310356**

The conventional design of the reception rooms could be opened up to give a kitchen/diner or a completey open-plan living area if you wanted to be more radical.

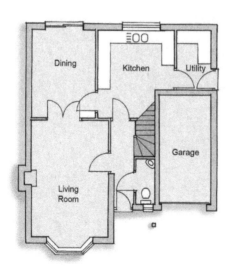

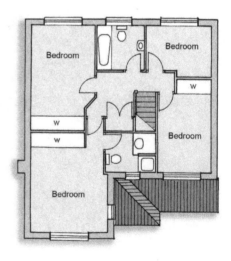

Plan no. **BHP 310197**

Another period style house, this one with a half tile-hung exterior, which would look good in many a village setting.

Traditional style

Floor area
125m²
1345ft²

Bedrooms
4

Bathrooms
2

Floors
2

Key features
Separate dining room
Utility room
Master en-suite

Garaging for
0 cars

Design
Potton

www.potton.co.uk
contact@potton.co.uk
01767 676 400

Build cost
£130,500

Design © Potton

Traditional style

Floor area
133m²
1432ft²

Bedrooms
4

Bathrooms
1

Floors
2

Key features
Open-plan living
Utility room

Garaging for
0 cars

Design
Architecture Plus

www.architecture-plus.co.uk
01934 416416

Build cost
£122,000

Design © Architecture Plus

Plan no. **BHP 310173**

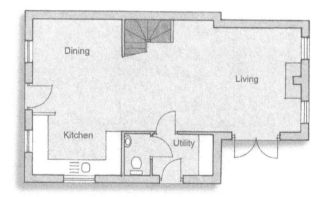

The shape of this cottage
would make it ideal for
a narrow or infill plot –
especially where the visual
impact from the kerb
needs to be minimised.

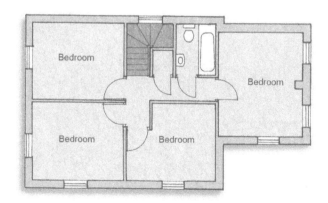

Plan no. **BHP 310989**

The catslide roof over the garage and porch add interest to this straightforward design.

Garage

Kitchen

Living Room

Dining Room

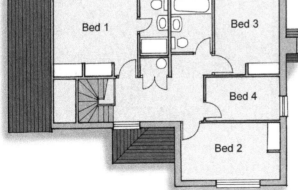

Bed 1

Bed 3

Bed 4

Bed 2

Traditional style

Floor area
138m²
1485ft²

Bedrooms
4

Bathrooms
2

Floors
2

Key features
Kitchen/breakfast room
Separate dining room
Study
Utility room
Master bed en-suite

Garaging for
2 cars

Design
Planahome

www.planahome.uk.com
plans@planahome.uk.com
01326 373600

Build cost
£127,000

Design © Planahome

Plan no. **BHP 310200**

This developer-style design ticks all of the boxes for standard spec – including the double garage, kitchen/breakfast room and master en-suite.

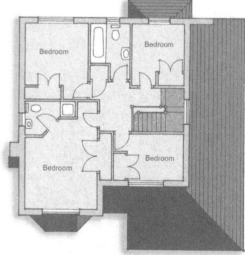

Plan no. **BHP 310395**

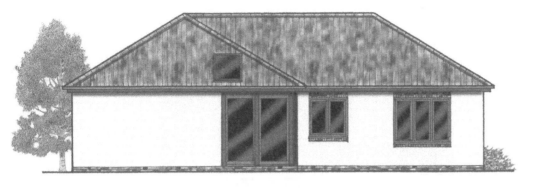

Four bedrooms, a large living room with 'bring the outside in' folding doors and a family-sized kitchen make up house-sized accommodation in a single storey.

Traditional style

Floor area
140m²
1507ft²

Bedrooms
4

Bathrooms
2

Floors
1

Key features
Kitchen/diner
Master bed en-suite

Garaging for
0 cars

Design
Architecture Plus

www.architecture-plus.co.uk
01934 416416

Build cost
£129,000

Design © Architecture Plus

Traditional style

Floor area
143m²
1539ft²

Bedrooms
4

Bathrooms
2

Floors
2

Key features
Master en-suite

Garaging for
1 car

Design
Architecture Plus

www.architecture-plus.co.uk
01934 416416

Build cost
£131,500

Design © Architecture Plus

Plan no. **BHP 310737**

This house offers a compact package with inbuilt garage and would work well on a smaller plot. It also packs in four bedrooms, a bathroom and en-suite.

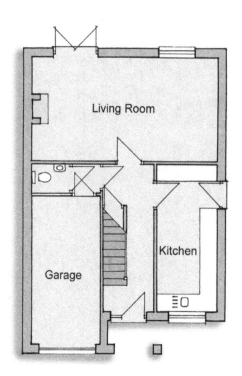

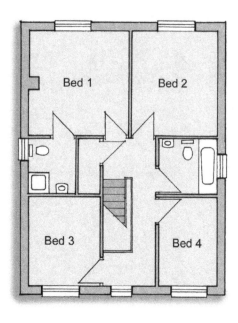

Plan no. **BHP 310797**

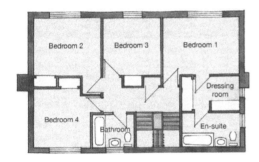

Featuring a compact kitchen, hall and dining room with four bedrooms upstairs. The decorative detail such as timberwork and small half-hip on the garage roof add visual interest.

Traditional style

Floor area
143m²
1539ft²

Bedrooms
4

Bathrooms
2

Floors
2

Key features
Kitchen/breakfast room
Utility room
Separate dining room
Master bedroom suite

Garaging for
1 car

Design
**David Bateman/
Oregon Homes**

Build cost
£131,500

Design © Oregon Homes

Traditional style

Floor area
144m²
1550ft²

Bedrooms
4

Bathrooms
2

Floors
2

Key features
Kitchen/breakfast room
Study
Linked lounge/diner
Master en-suite

Garaging for
0 cars

Design
Planahome

www.planahome.uk.com
plans@planahome.uk.com
01326 373600

Build cost
£132,500

Design © Planahome

Plan no. **BHP 310038**

A long porch, supported by an impressive brick pillar, adds a twist to the front of this design. Inside the hall leads on to twin reception rooms a kitchen and study. Upstairs there are three double and one single bedrooms.

Plan no. **BHP 310668**

Through the covered porch the hall leads through to an open-plan living area. Upstairs bedrooms two and three are amply proportioned and share a good-sized family bathroom.

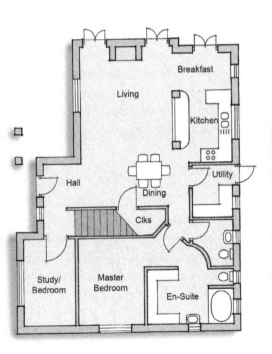

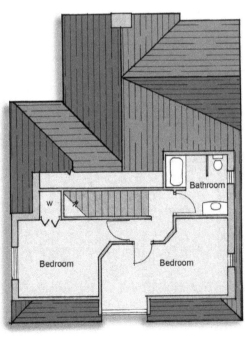

Traditional style

Floor area
147m²
1582ft²

Bedrooms
4

Bathrooms
2

Floors
2

Key features
Open-plan living
Utility room
Master en-suite

Garaging for
0 cars

Design
Jeremy Rawlings

www.periodhome.net 01884
266444

Build cost
£135,000

Design © Jeremy Rawlings

Traditional style

Floor area

147m²

1582ft²

Bedrooms

4

Bathrooms

2

Floors

2

Key features
Utility room
Linked lounge/diner
Study
Master en-suite

Garaging for
0 cars

Design
**JS Building
Consultancy**

www.ukbuildingconsultancy.
co.uk
jsharples@ricsonline.org
0113 250 1303

Build cost
£135,000

Plan no. **BHP 310233**

Eyebrow dormer windows lend a cottage look to this design. Inside, the layout of reception rooms is as traditional as the look with a separate dining room. Upstairs are four double bedrooms.

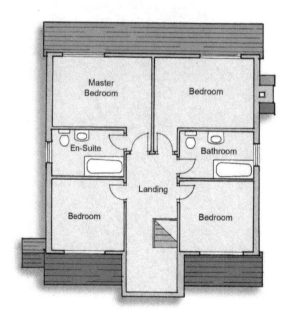

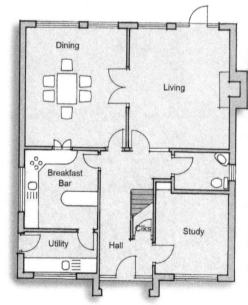

Plan no. **BHP 310083**

The protruding garage gives the opportunity to create a balcony for the en-suite bedroom and a sheltered approach to the front door. Accomodation includes kitchen/dining room, a large living room and four double bedrooms.

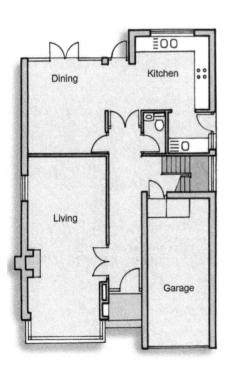

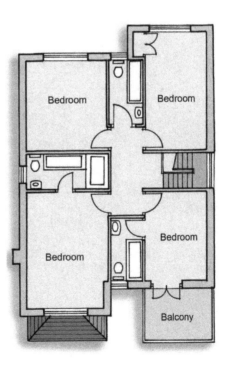

Traditional style

Floor area
149m²
1604ft²

Bedrooms
4

Bathrooms
3

Floors
2

Key features
Kitchen/dining room
Balcony
Two en-suites

Garaging for
1 car

Design
**John Shida
(Morningtide
Developments)**
www.morningtide.fsnet.co.uk
johnshida@morningtide.
fsnet.co.uk
01621 815485

Build cost
£137,000

Design © John Shida

Traditional style

Floor area
152m²
1636ft²

Bedrooms
4

Bathrooms
4

Floors
2

Key features
Kitchen/breakfast room
Dining conservatory
Family room
Utility room
Two en-suites

Garaging for
0 cars

Design
Planahome

www.planahome.uk.com
plans@planahome.uk.com
01326 373600

Build cost
£140,000

Design © Planahome

Plan no. **BHP 310731**

This home would make the best of a sunny spot with its extensively glazed dining room and lounge areas. Upstairs a galleried landing leads on to three bedrooms, two en-suites and a decent-sized family bathroom.

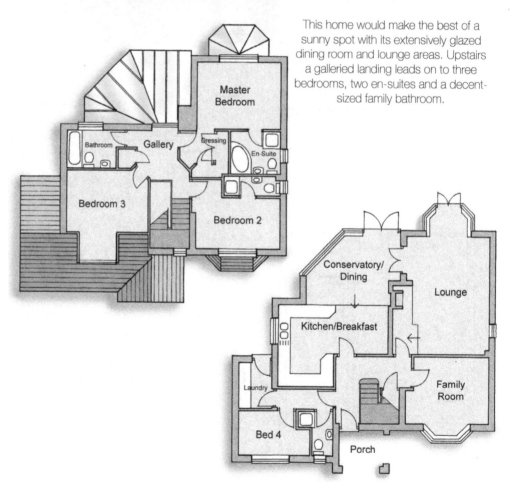

Plan no. **BHP 310443**

In spite of being a basic box the detailing on this design lifts it out of the ordinary. Inside there is a kitchen/dining room and separate lounge and study.

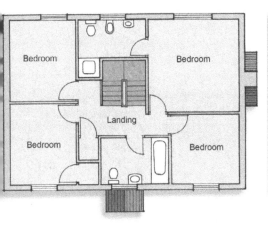

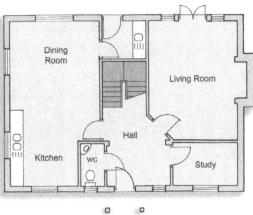

Traditional style

Floor area
152m²
1636ft²

Bedrooms
4

Bathrooms
2

Floors
2

Key features
Kitchen/dining room
Study
Master en-suite

Garaging for
0 cars

Design
Potton

www.potton.co.uk
contact@potton.co.uk
01767 676 400

Build cost
£140,000

Design © Potton

Traditional style

Floor area

153m²

1647ft²

Bedrooms

4

Bathrooms

2

Floors

2

Key features
Open-plan living
Master en-suite

Garaging for
0 cars

Design
Potton

www.potton.co.uk
contact@potton.co.uk
01767 676 400

Build cost
£141,000

Design © Potton

Plan no. **BHP 310617**

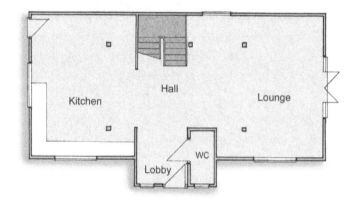

Open-plan downstairs and
four bedrooms upstairs - three
of which are lit by Velux-
style windows. The master
bedroom comes with en-suite
while the other three beds
share a family bathroom.

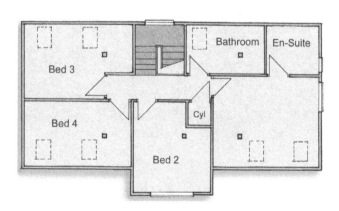

Plan no. **BHP 310359**

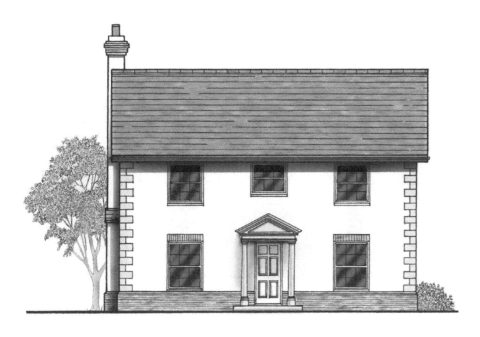

The living room has triple-aspect windows and in the kitchen/breakfast room there are French doors to the garden. There is a Georgian feel to this design with the classically-influenced porch.

Bedroom
Bedroom
Landing
Bedroom
Bedroom

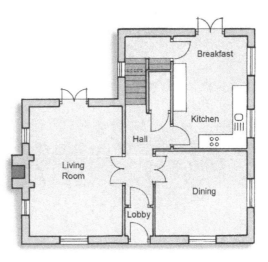

Breakfast
Kitchen
Hall
Living Room
Dining
Lobby

Traditional style

Floor area
154m²
1658ft²

Bedrooms
4

Bathrooms
2

Floors
2

Key features
Kitchen/breakfast room
Separate dining room
Porch
Master en-suite

Garaging for
0 cars

Design
Custom Homes

www.customhomes.co.uk
admin@customhomes.co.uk
01787 377388

Build cost
£141,500

Design © Custom Homes

Traditional style

Floor area
159m²
1711ft²

Bedrooms
4

Bathrooms
3

Floors
2

Key features
Sun lounge
Kitchen/dining room
Utility room
Two en-suites
Vaulted bedroom

Garaging for
1 car

Design
**John Braid
(at Leslie R Hutt)**

lhuttarchitect@btinternet.com
01463 235566

Build cost
£146,000

Design © John Braid

Plan no. **BHP 310329**

Inside this house benefits from generous areas of glazing and full-height ceilings to give a light, contemporary feel. The living areas are designed to flow through from each other. The first floor features three well-proportioned bedrooms set neatly into the eaves.

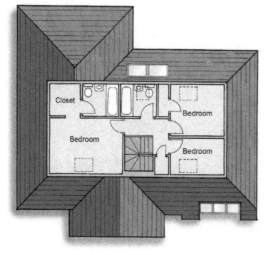

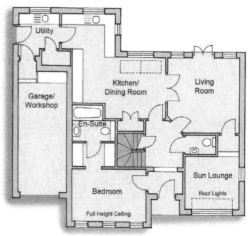

Plan no. **BHP 310368**

This design incorporates a dining hall, a combined kitchen and breakfast room and two bedrooms on the ground floor. Upstairs there are two further bedrooms, a balcony and a bathroom.

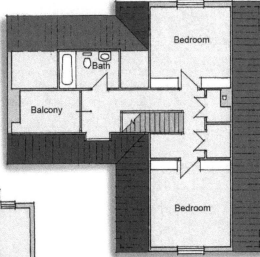

Traditional style

Floor area

160m²

1722ft²

Bedrooms

4

Bathrooms

2

Floors

2

Key features
Kitchen/dining room
Dining hall
Utility room
Balcony
Master en-suite

Garaging for
0 cars

Design
Design & Materials

www.designandmaterials.uk.com
enquiries@designandmaterials.
uk.com
01909 540 123

Build cost
£147,000

Traditional style

Floor area

160m²

1722ft²

Bedrooms

4

Bathrooms

2

Floors

2

Key features
Kitchen/breafast room
Lounge/dining room
Utility room
Master bed en-suite

Garaging for
0cars

Design
Design & Materials

www.designandmaterials.uk.com
enquiries@designandmaterials.
uk.com
01909 540 123

Build cost
£147,000

Plan no. **BHP 310905**

The ground floor of this house is open-plan and the living room and dining room are separated only by a feature fireplace. The kitchen is accessed through a wide opening marked by twin feature posts. The first floor has a galleried landing and four bedrooms with one en-suite.

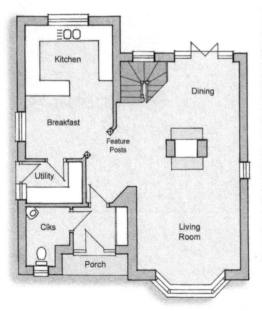

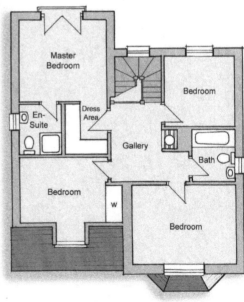

Plan no. **BHP 310710**

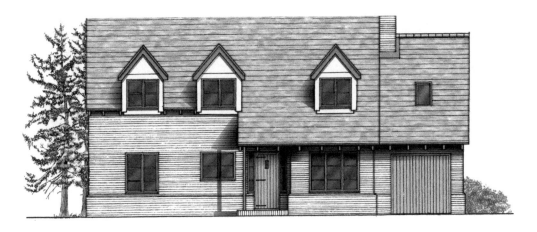

This family home has a vaulted ceiling in the master bedroom while a double-height hallway with gallery add to the impression of space. Downstairs there is an inglenook fireplace and separate dining room.

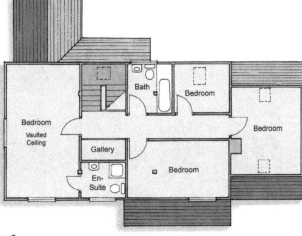

Bedroom
Vaulted Ceiling

Bath

Bedroom

Bedroom

Gallery

Bedroom

En-Suite

Breakfast

Utility

WC

Kitchen

Living Room

Garage

Dining

Study

Traditional style

Floor area
160m²
1722ft²

Bedrooms
4

Bathrooms
2

Floors
2

Key features
Kitchen/breakfast room
Utility room
Study
Separate dining room
Vaulted master bed

Garaging for
1 car

Design
Potton

www.potton.co.uk
contact@potton.co.uk
01767 676 400

Build cost
£147,000

Design © Potton

Barn style

Floor area
161m²
1733 ft²

Bedrooms
4

Bathrooms
2

Floors
2

Key features
Double-height lounge
Kitchen/diner
Utility room
Master en-suite

Garaging for
0 cars

Design
Welsh Oak Frame

www.welshoakframe.com
01686 688000

Build cost
£148,000

Design © Welsh Oak Frame

Plan no. **BHP 310494**

The first floor of this house works as two separate mezzanine levels each with their own staircase. This design allows for a stunning double-height ceiling above the living room.

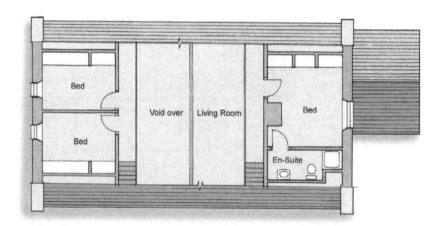

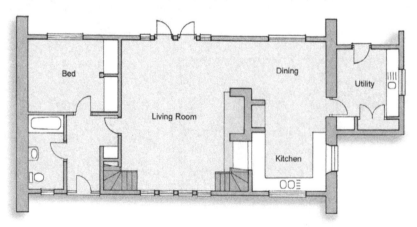

Plan no. **BHP** **310425**

Folding doors brings the outside in to the key living areas in this design. The single-storey building has room for four bedrooms but there's space for a staircase if you want to use the generous loft area for more sleeping accommodation later on and a velux is already in place to provide light.

Traditional style

Floor area
162m²
1744 ft²

Bedrooms
4

Bathrooms
2

Floors
1

Key features
Kitchen/dining room
Utility room
Music room
Master en-suite

Garaging for
1 car

Design
Design & Materials

www.designandmaterials.uk.com
enquiries@designandmaterials.uk.com
01909 540 123

Build cost
£140,000

Design © Design &
Materials

Traditional style

Floor area

162m²

1744ft²

Bedrooms

4

Bathrooms

2

Floors

2

Key features
Kitchen/breakfast room
Separate dining room
Utility room
Study
Master en-suite

Garaging for
0cars

Design
Design & Materials

www.designandmaterials.uk.com
enquiries@designandmaterials.
uk.com
01909 540 123

Build cost
£149,000

Plan no. **BHP 310560**

This design manages to fit a breakfast area into the kitchen as well as a separate dining room, study and utility room. Upstairs three of the bedrooms feature built-in wardrobes - and for the master there's an en-suite.

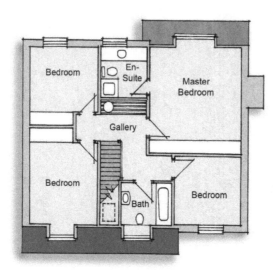

Plan no. **BHP 310800**

Open-plan living space gives maximum flexibility downstairs and there's also an en-suite master bedroom with French doors onto the patio/garden. Upstairs Velux-type windows and dormers light the three bedrooms and bathroom.

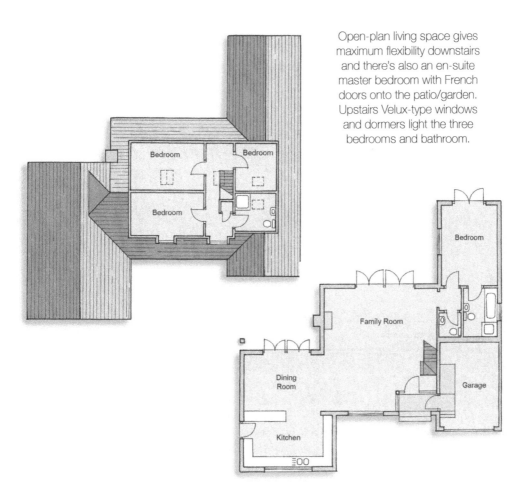

Traditional style

Floor area
162m²
1744ft²

Bedrooms
4

Bathrooms
2

Floors
2

Key features
Open-plan living
Master bed en-suite

Garaging for
1 car

Design
**John Shida
(Morningtide
Developments)**

www.morningtide.fsnet.co.uk
johnshida@morningtide.
fsnet.co.uk
01621 815485

Build cost
£149,000

Design © John Shida

Contemporary style

Floor area
168m²
1808ft²

Bedrooms
4

Bathrooms
2

Floors
2

Key features
Conservatory
Sauna
Courtyard
Lap pool
Basement

Garaging for
0 cars

Design
Architecture Plus

www.architecture-plus.co.uk
01934 416416

Build cost
£154,500

Design © Architecture Plus

Plan no. **BHP 310677**

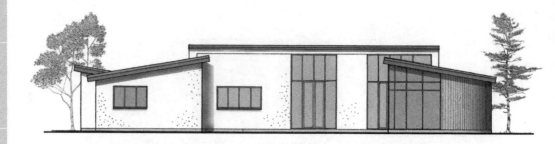

This design uses separate wings to create defined living, relaxing and sleeping spaces. The conservatory with its built-in sauna is accessed from a bridge from the main sleeping area which leads onto the kitchen and dining area via the entrance hall and its pretty courtyard.

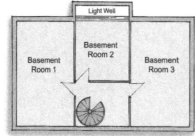

Plan no. **BHP 310104**

Lots of interesting external detail and roof lines add to the appeal of this design. There's plenty of space in the kitchen/family area thanks to the conservatory and upstairs there are four bedrooms and two en-suite shower rooms.

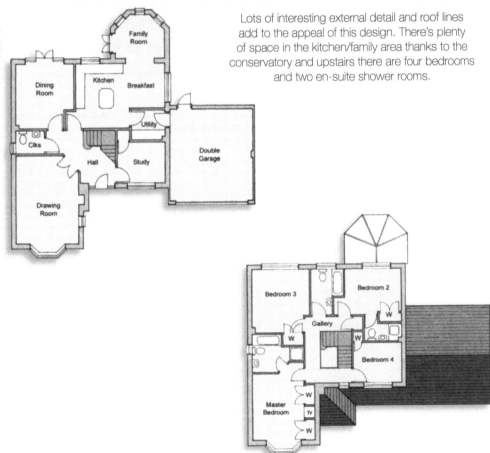

Traditional style

Floor area
170m²
1830ft²

Bedrooms
4

Bathrooms
3

Floors
2

Key features
Kitchen/family room
Study
Separate dining room
Galleried landing
2 beds en-suite

Garaging for
2 cars

Design
Planahome

www.planahome.uk.com
plans@planahome.uk.com
01326 373600

Build cost
£156,400

Traditional style

Floor area
170m²
1830ft²

Bedrooms
4

Bathrooms
3

Floors
2

Key features
Kitchen/breakfast room
Separate dining room
Study
Master en-suite
2nd en-suite

Garaging for
0 cars

Design
Design & Materials

www.designandmaterials.uk.com
enquiries@designandmaterials.
uk.com
01909 540 123

Build cost
£156,400

Design © Design &
Materials

Plan no. **BHP 310662**

This design has the look of a cottage but the accommodation of a family-sized house with two en-suite bedrooms, two single bedrooms and lots of living space on the ground floor.

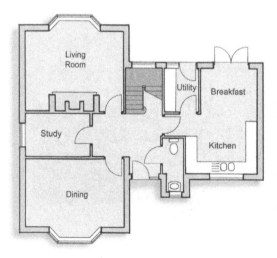

Plan no. **BHP 310539**

This house features a big hall and internal access to the garage. The kitchen and dining room could be combined to create more open-plan accomodation. Upstairs the master bedroom has its own en-suite.

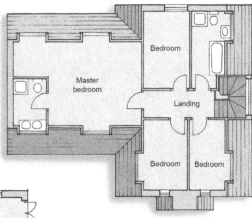

Bedroom

Master bedroom

Landing

Bedroom

Bedroom

Kitchen

Dining

Garage

Hall

WC

C

Living

Traditional style

Floor area
171m²
1841ft²

Bedrooms
4

Bathrooms
2

Floors
2

Key features
Separate dining room
Master en-suite

Garaging for
1 car

Design
Custom Homes

www.customhomes.co.uk
admin@customhomes.co.uk
01787 377388

Build cost
£157,000

Design © Custom Homes

Traditional style

Floor area
172m²
1851ft²

Bedrooms
4

Bathrooms
2

Floors
2

Key features
Kitchen/dining room
Boot room
Study

Garaging for
2 cars

Design
Border Oak

www.borderoak.com s
ales@borderoak.com
01568 708752

Build cost
£158,000

Design © Border Oak

Plan no. **BHP 310041**

Lots of external period features including a half-hipped roof on the garage, brick arches over the windows and open timber work on the porch front. Inside there is a large kitchen/ family area and sparate sitting room.

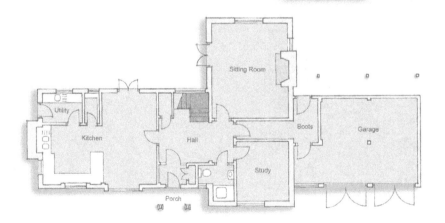

Plan no. **BHP 310221**

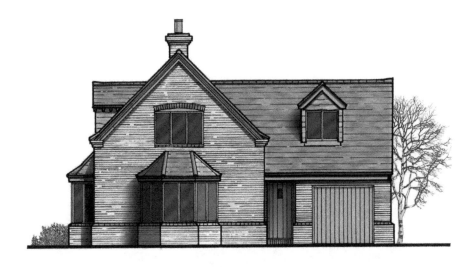

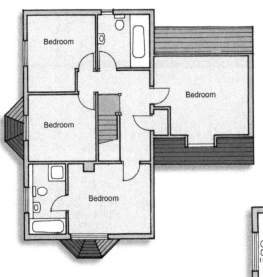

Dormer and bay windows punctuate this design's lines and add extra light into the rooms. The kitchen, dining area and living room are all linked by double doors. Upstairs the roof space above the garage has been used to create room for a fourth bedroom.

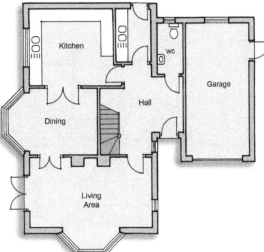

Traditional style

Floor area
172m²
1851ft²

Bedrooms
4

Bathrooms
2

Floors
2

Key features
Utility room
Separate dining room
Master en-suite

Garaging for
1 car

Design
Potton

www.potton.co.uk
contact@potton.co.uk
01767 676 400

Build cost
£158,000

Design © Potton

Traditional style

Floor area
173m²
1862ft²

Bedrooms
4

Bathrooms
3

Floors
2

Key features
Kitchen/breakfast room
Utility room
Separate dining room
Study
2 en-suite bedrooms

Garaging for
0 cars

Design
Planahome

www.planahome.uk.com
plans@planahome.uk.com
01326 373600

Build cost
£160,000

Design © Planahome

Plan no. **BHP   310146**

Two en-suite bedrooms, a dressing area for the master suite and a lounge and separate dining room are amongst the features in this design.

Plan no. **BHP 310887**

This Tudor-look house has plenty of living space and four double bedrooms. Smart touches include a balcony, a large double garage and a covered outside store.

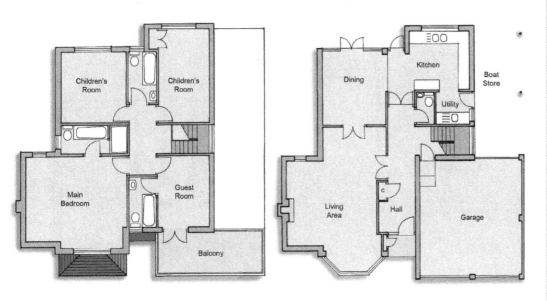

Traditional style

Floor area
173m²
1862ft²

Bedrooms
4

Bathrooms
3

Floors
2

Key features
Kitchen/dining room
Utility room
Two en-suites
Balcony

Garaging for
2 cars

Design
**John Shida
(Morningtide
Developments)**
www.morningtide.fsnet.co.uk
johnshida@morningtide.
fsnet.co.uk
01621 815485

Build cost
£160,000

Design © John Shida

Traditional style

Floor area

176m²

1894ft²

Bedrooms

4

Bathrooms

2

Floors

2

Key features
Study
Separate dining room
Master en-suite

Garaging for
1 car

Design
Custom Homes

www.customhomes.co.uk
admin@customhomes.co.uk
01787 377388

Build cost
£162,000

Design © Custom Homes

Plan no. **BHP 310791**

The hall is kept small to allow the available space to be used in the reception rooms. Upstairs the master bedroom has an en-suite shower room.

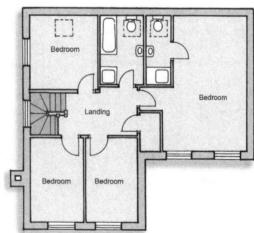

Plan no. **BHP 310569**

Inside the layout offers four bedrooms on the first floor, three reception rooms downstairs and a kitchen/utility area.

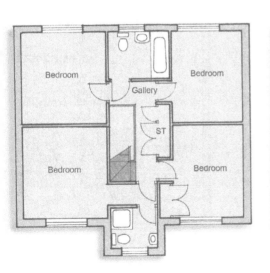

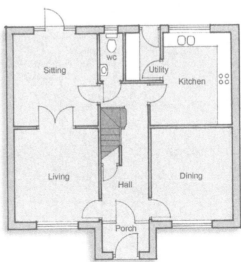

Traditional style

Floor area
177m²
1905ft²

Bedrooms
4

Bathrooms
2

Floors
2

Key features
Living/sitting room
Separate dining room
Utility room
Porch
Master en-suite

Garaging for
0 cars

Design
Architecture Plus

www.architecture-plus.co.uk
01934 416416

Build cost
£163,000

Design © Architecture Plus

Traditional style

Floor area
178m²
1916ft²

Bedrooms
4

Bathrooms
2

Floors
2

Key features
Lounge/dining room
Utility room
Master bed en-suite

Garaging for
1 car

Design
Churchill Design

www.churchilldesign.co.uk
info@churchilldesign.co.uk
01252 325701

Build cost
£164,000

Design © Churchill Design

Plan no. **BHP 310770**

The basic layout of this house still manages to fit in an en-suite for the master bedroom
and a utility next to the kitchen.

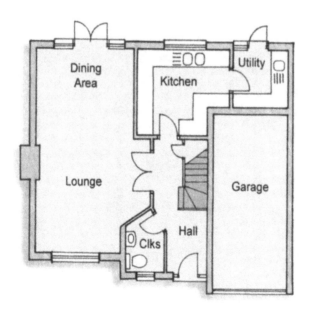

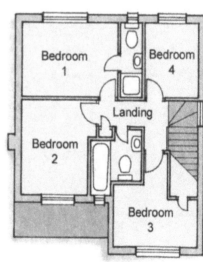

Plan no. **BHP 311004**

Interesting features in this design include access to the integral garage through the utility room and a dining area adjacent to the lounge. There is also space for a play room and study as well as the four bedrooms – one of which is en-suite.

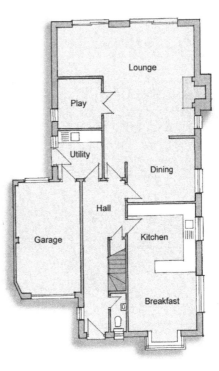

Traditional style

Floor area

180m²

1938ft²

Bedrooms

4

Bathrooms

2

Floors

2

Key features
Kitchen/dining room
Utility room
Study
Master en-suite
Dressing room

Garaging for
0cars

Design
Border Oak

www.borderoak.com
sales@borderoak.com
01568 708752

Build cost
£165,500

Design © Border Oak

Plan no. **BHP 310449**

The timber exterior detailing on this house gives it a vaguely 'Arts & Crafts' feel, as does the porch. The large hall is also in keeping with this style – as is the galleried landing.

Plan no. **BHP 310590**

The twin dormers and central entrance bay create symmetry in this design. The family room sits conveniently between the kitchen and lounge. The single-storey garage wing adds interest to the design as well as extra space for a utility room, downstairs cloakroom and a store. The first floor features a master suite, three double bedrooms and a large family bathroom.

Traditional style

Floor area
181m²
1948 ft²

Bedrooms
4

Bathrooms
2

Floors
2

Key features
Kitchen/dining
Family room
Utility room
Master en-suite

Garaging for
2 cars

Design
Reed Architects

01544 260523

Build cost
£166,500

Barn style

Floor area

181m²

1948 ft²

Bedrooms

4

Bathrooms

2

Floors

2

Key features
Separate dining room
Study
Utility room
Double-height hall
Master bed en-suite

Garaging for
2 cars

Design
Custom Homes

www.customhomes.co.uk
admin@customhomes.co.uk
01787 377388

Build cost
£166,500

Design © Custom Homes

Plan no. **BHP 310263**

The double-height entrance hall with a staircase which divides
at half-landing level adds to the barnlike feel of this design. If
you can't find a barn to convert, why not build one?

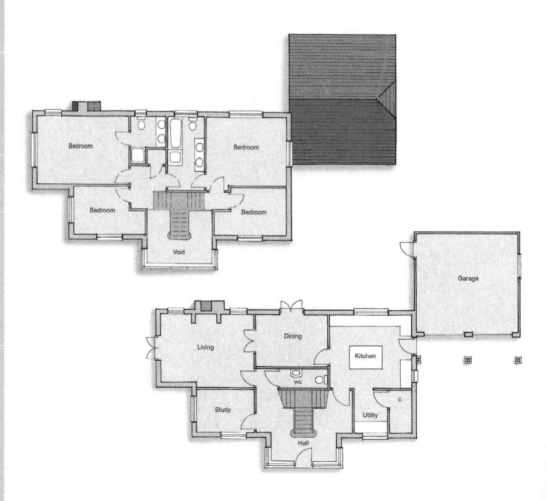

Plan no. **BHP 310101**

An exciting mix of turrets, levels and materials makes this an intersting design. The turrett creates a Scottish feel and there is a dining hall and a large first floor living room with triple aspect windows and a balcony.

Floor area
183m²
1970ft²

Bedrooms
4

Bathrooms
2

Floors
2

Key features
Dining hall
Utility room
Garden store
Master en-suite

Garaging for
1 car

Design
The Border Design Centre

www.borderdesign.co.uk
borderdesign@btconnect.com
01578 740218

Build cost
£165,500

Design © The Border Design Centre

Traditional style

Floor area
185m²
1991ft²

Bedrooms
4

Bathrooms
2

Floors
3

Key features
Open-plan living
space
Separate lounge
Utility room

Garaging for
0cars

Design
Churchill Design

www.churchilldesign.co.uk
info@churchilldesign.co.uk
01252 325701

Build cost
£170,000

Design © Churchill Design

Plan no. **BHP 310284**

How do you pack four bedrooms into a narrow plot? Simple, add a second floor with a top-floor en-suit bedroom. Downstairs the living area is open-plan with a sitting room that can be shut off by closing a pair of double doors.

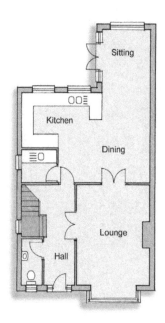

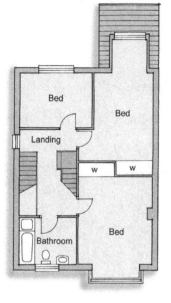

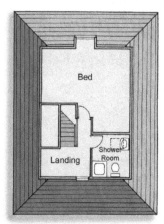

Plan no. **BHP 310461**

The brick, render and tile façade set off this family home and would help it blend in many locations. The key living areas are arranged in an open, flowing style and there's a well-lit galleried landing leading to four double bedrooms upstairs.

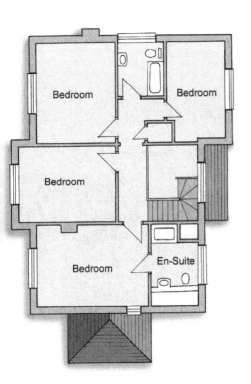

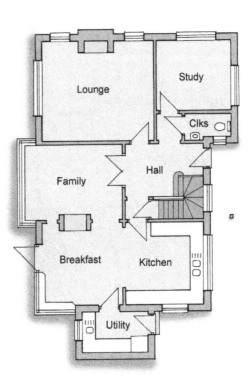

Traditional style

Floor area

186m²

2002ft²

Bedrooms

4

Bathrooms

2

Floors

2

Key features
Kitchen/breakfast room
Family room
Study
Utility room
Master en-suite

Garaging for
0 cars

Design
Opus Architecture and Design

01252 861759

£

Build cost
£171,000

Traditional style

Floor area

187m²

2013ft²

Bedrooms

4

Bathrooms

3

Floors

2

Key features
Kitchen/dining room
Study
Utility room
Car port
2 beds en-suite

Garaging for
1 car

Design

Potton

www.potton.co.uk
contact@potton.co.uk
01767 676 400

£

Build cost
£172,000

Design © Potton

Plan no. **BHP 310854**

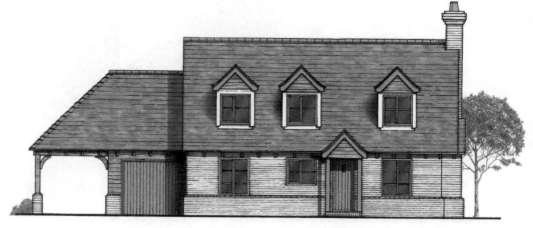

This design has a living room which runs the full depth of the house and features an inglenook fireplace. Upstairs the master bedroom features an en-suite shower room and walk-in wardrobe and the second bedroom an en-suite bathroom.

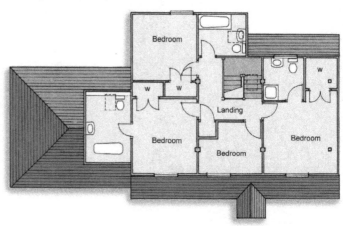

Plan no. **BHP 310377**

Once through the porch you enter a full-width open-plan lounge and dining hall. The kitchen and family room also provide plenty of space. The first floor has three bedrooms and a master suite while the attic room could house an office or play area.

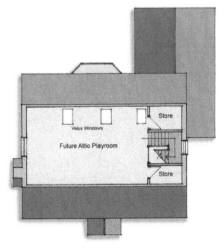

Traditional style

Floor area
190m²
2045ft²

Bedrooms
4

Bathrooms
2

Floors
3

Key features
Vaulted family room
Living room/dining hall
Study
Master en-suite
Attic playroom

Garaging for
0 cars

Design
Design & Materials

www.designandmaterials.uk.com
enquiries@designandmaterials.uk.com
01909 540 123

Build cost
£175,000

Design © Design & Materials

Traditional style

Floor area
190m²
2045ft²

Bedrooms
4

Bathrooms
3

Floors
2

Key features
Kitchen/family room
Utility room
study
Separate dining room
2 beds en-suite

Garaging for
2 cars

Design
Design & Materials

www.designandmaterials.uk.com
enquiries@designandmaterials.
uk.com
01909 540 123

Build cost
£175,000

Design © Design &
Materials

Plan no. **BHP 310713**

This double-fronted home features an L-shaped kitchen/family room and large living room. Upstairs the master and second bedrooms share a balcony but each gets its own en-suite bathroom.

Plan no. **BHP 310479**

The deep bay window on this house design creates lots of extra space in the living room and bedroom above. The house also offers a separate study, a first floor sitting area and a combined kitchen and breakfast room.

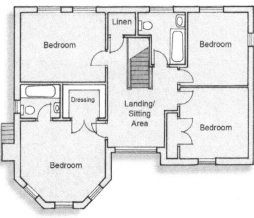

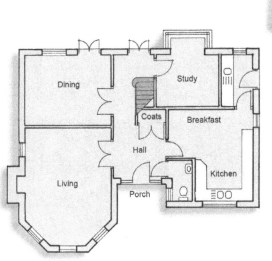

Traditional style

Floor area
192m²
2067ft²

Bedrooms
4

Bathrooms
2

Floors
2

Key features
Kitchen/breakfast room
Separate dining room
Study
Utility room
Master en-suite

Garaging for
0 cars

Design
The Bespoke Design Company

www.planahome.uk.com
plans@planahome.uk.com
01326 373600

Build cost
£177,000

Design © The Bespoke Design Company

Traditional style

Floor area

202m²

2174ft²

Bedrooms

4

Bathrooms

2

Floors

2

Key features
Kitchen/breakfast room
Separate dining room
Family room
Galleried landing
Master bed en-suite

Garaging for
0 cars

Design
**Gordon Melrose
Building Design**

www.gmbuildingdesign.
co.uk enquiries@gmbuild-
ingdesign.co.uk
01750 725333

Build cost
£186,000

Design © Gordon Melrose
Building Design

Plan no. **BHP 310515**

Either side of the hall, with its cloakroom and storage, is a twin-aspect living room and family room. An open-plan dining and kitchen area takes up the back of the house. The first floor features a 360 degree gallery around the staircase, three double bedrooms and a master suite with its own balcony.

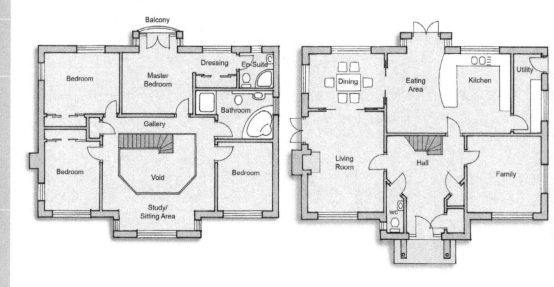

Plan no. **BHP 310656**

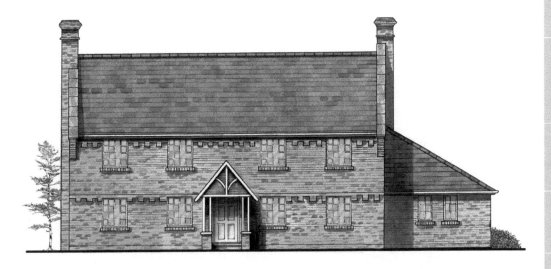

Traditional style

Floor area
203m²
2185ft²

Bedrooms
4

Bathrooms
2

Floors
2

The ground floor offers open-plan living but with the ability to close sliding or hinged doors to create a more conventional layout. The first floor layout is more formal and features a galleried landing, a full-depth master suite and three further bedrooms.

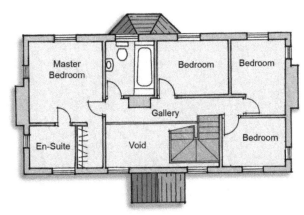

Master Bedroom

Bedroom

Bedroom

Gallery

En-Suite

Void

Bedroom

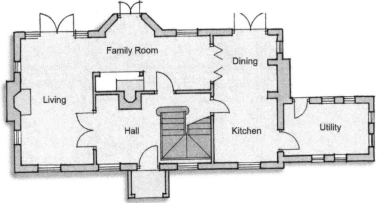

Family Room

Dining

Living

Hall

Kitchen

Utility

Key features
Galleried landing
Double-height hall
Family room
Kitchen/diner
Large utility room

Garaging for
0 cars

Design
Jeremy Rawlings

www.periodhome.net
01884 266444

Build cost
£187,000

Traditional style

Floor area
203m²
2185ft²

Bedrooms
4

Bathrooms
3

Floors
2

Key features
Kitchen/family room
Conservatory
Study
Utility room
2 beds en-suite

Garaging for
2 cars

Design
**The Bespoke
Design Company**

www.planahome.uk.com
plans@planahome.uk.com
01326 373600

£

Build cost
£187,000

Design © The Bespoke
Design Company

Plan no. **BHP 310650**

The main entrance is at the side leaving the impressive double-frontage free for separate twin French door access to the family room and kitchen. At the rear of the house part of the conservatory goes double height creating a great view from the galleried landing on the first floor. Four bedrooms and three bathrooms complete the picture upstairs.

Plan no. **BHP 310266**

Go through the porch and vestibule and you're in a dining/living room divided by a feature fireplace. The kitchen and breakfast area are similarly open-plan and lead onto a family room. Upstairs all but one of the bedrooms has its own en-suite and the master bedroom gets its own balcony and dressing room.

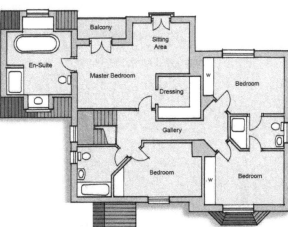

Balcony

Sitting Area

En-Suite

Master Bedroom

Dressing

w

Bedroom

Gallery

Bedroom

Bedroom

w

Bedroom

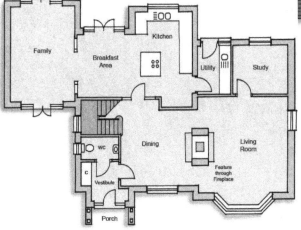

Family

Kitchen

Breakfast Area

Utility

Study

wc

Dining

Living Room

c

Feature through Fireplace

Vestibule

Porch

Traditional style

Floor area
204m²
2196ft²

Bedrooms
4

Bathrooms
3

Floors
2

Key features
Living/dining room
Kitchen/breakfast room
Family room
Study
Master bedroom suite

Garaging for
0 cars

Design
Design & Materials

www.designandmaterials.uk.com
enquiries@designandmaterials.uk.com
01909 540 123

Build cost
£187,500

Design © Design & Materials

Traditional style

Floor area
208m²
2239ft²

Bedrooms
4

Bathrooms
2

Floors
2

Key features
Kitchen/breakfast room
Separate dining room
Feature staircase
Study
Master en-suite

Garaging for
0cars

Design
Custom Homes

www.customhomes.co.uk
admin@customhomes.co.uk
01787 377388

Build cost
£191,000

Design © Custom Homes

Plan no. **BHP   310251**

There's an entrance hall with a feature central staircase, a large lounge and a kitchen/breakfast room that take up a whole side of the house each. Upstairs the master bedroom dominates one corner of the house with an en-suite bathroom and dressing room attached.

Plan no. **BHP 310614**

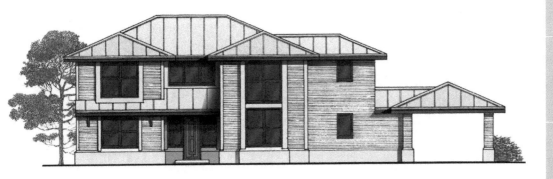

The master bedroom suite is twin-aspect with its own terrace. On the ground floor the layout offers an interesting arrangment of rooms with the option for the fourth bedroom to be used as a study.

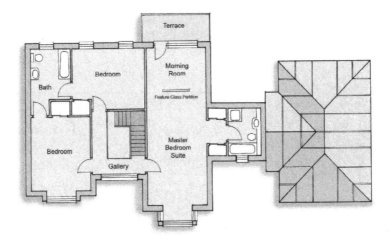

Terrace

Bedroom

Bath

Morning Room

Feature Glass Partition

Bedroom

Master Bedroom Suite

Gallery

Sunroom

Living Room

Kitchen

En-Suite

Entrance Hall

Utility

WC

Carport

Study/ Bedroom

Dining Room

Traditional style

Floor area

214m²

2302ft²

Bedrooms

4

Bathrooms

3

Floors

2

Key features
Kitchen/dining room
Large utility room
Galleried landing
2 beds en-suite

Garaging for
1 car

Design
Border Oak

www.borderoak.com
sales@borderoak.com
01568 708752

Build cost
£197,000

Design © Border Oak

Plan no. **BHP 310065**

The en-suite for the master bedroom is cleverly located in the roofspace over the utility room. On the ground floor the large hall could be used for dining and the utility offers direct access to the garage and the garden.

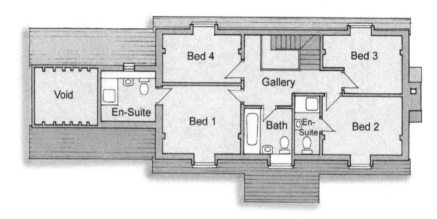

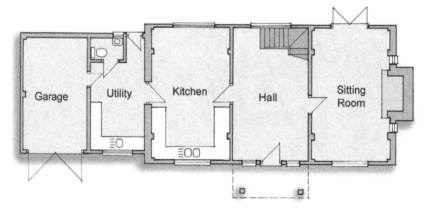

Plan no. **BHP 310029**

A house packed full of useful spaces including a study, garage, separate dining room and a master bedroom with a separate dressing room and dormer-windowed en-suite bathroom.

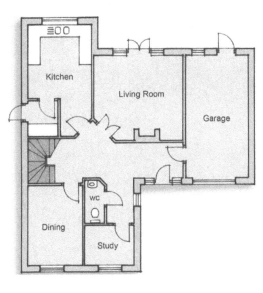

Traditional style

Floor area

216m²

2325ft²

Bedrooms

4

Bathrooms

3

Floors

2

Key features
Dining/family room
Study
Utility room
Galleried landing
2 beds en-suite

Garaging for
2 cars

Design
**John Braid
(at Leslie R Hutt)**

lhuttarchitect@btinternet.com
01463 235566

Build cost
£199,000

Plan no. **BHP 310191**

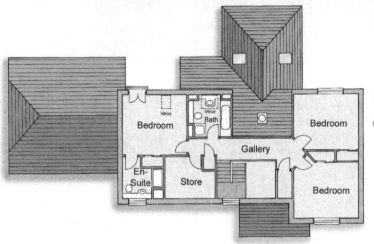

This house packs in a living room, family room, study, utility room and en-suite bedroom downstairs. Upstairs the galleried landing gives way to three further bedrooms.

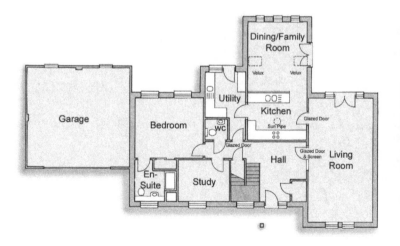

Plan no. **BHP 310743**

This house has plenty of natural light in the kitchen and hall. The garage extends right back and becomes an open-sided boat shed. All the rooms are large but you could add even more space by pushing up into the attic later on.

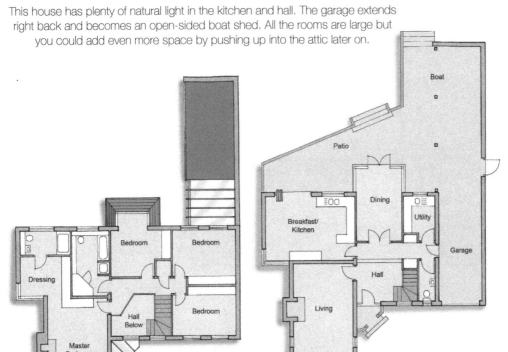

Traditional style

Floor area
220m²
2368ft²

Bedrooms
4

Bathrooms
2

Floors
2

Key features
Kitchen/breakfast room
Separate dining room
Boat/car port
Master dressing area
Galleried landing

Garaging for
1 car

Design
Fine Modern Homes (R.Robins)

www.finemodernhomes.co.uk
01225 777727

Build cost
£202,500

Design © Fine Modern Homes

Traditional style

Floor area
222m²
2390ft²

Bedrooms
4

Bathrooms
2

Floors
2

Key features
Separate dining room
Utility room
Study
Office
Master en-suite

Garaging for
0 cars

Design
Border Oak

www.borderoak.com
sales@borderoak.com
01568 708752

Build cost
£199,000

Plan no. **BHP 310755**

The house will appeal to many who enjoy a lifestyle based around the kitchen.
There is also a separate dining room for entertaining, a study, utility room and larder.
Upstairs there is a galleried landing and master bedroom with en-suite shower room.

Plan no. **BHP 310362**

Unusually the front door and utility room door are on the same aspect of this design. One benfit can be that shopping being unloaded from the car can be taken straight into the utility room/ kitchen. The master bedroom offers an en-suite and dressing room.

Traditional style

Floor area

222m²

2390ft²

Bedrooms

4

Bathrooms

3

Floors

2

Key features
Kitchen/breakfast room
Study
Separate dining room
Master bedroom suite
Galleried landing

Garaging for
0 cars

Design
Design & Materials

www.designandmaterials.uk.com
enquiries@designandmaterials.
uk.com
01909 540 123

Build cost
£199,000

Traditional style

Floor area
223m²
2400ft²

Bedrooms
4

Bathrooms
4

Floors
2

Key features
Lobby
Kitchen/family room
Dining hall
Sudy
2 beds en-suite

Garaging for
0 cars

Design
**The Bespoke
Design Company**

www.planahome.uk.com
plans@planahome.uk.com
01326 373600

Build cost
£200,000

Design © The Bespoke
Design Company

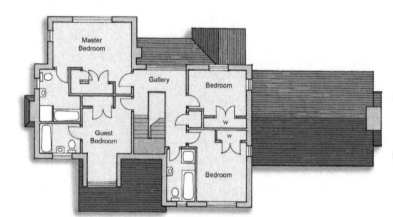

The splayed walls of
the porch give a feeling
of solidity as well as a
period look which is re-
enforced by the number
of chimneys. There are
open fires in the familly
room and living room.
Upstairs there is a guest
bedroom with en-suite
as well as a master
bedroom with en-suite.

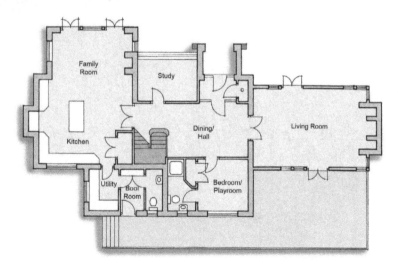

Plan no. **BHP 310587**

The upstairs of this design offers a reading area as well as a dressing room and shower room for the master bedroom.

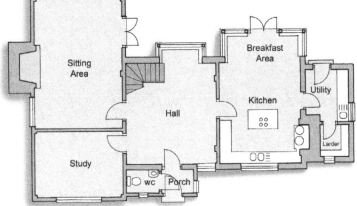

Traditional style

Floor area
225m²
2422ft²

Bedrooms
4

Bathrooms
3

Floors
2

Key features
Dining hall
Kitchen/day room
Study
Self-contained flat
Workshop

Garaging for
2 cars

Design
Welsh Oak Frame

www.welshoakframe.com
01686 688000

Build cost
£202,000

Design © Welsh Oak Frame

Plan no. **BHP 310992**

From the double-height dining hall with twin staircases to the linked reception rooms this house sets out to offer a range of facilities. Designed to offer a 'granny annexe' over the double garage this hosue gets over the problem of locating it on the first floor by having space for a lift.

Plan no. **BHP 310551**

The part-timbered gable of this design overhangs the entrance. Behind the staircase the double-height dining hall leads onto the kitchen and living room. These rooms all have doors opening onto the garden. Upstairs there are four double bedrooms, twin en-suites and a big family bathroom.

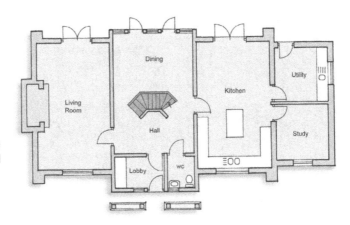

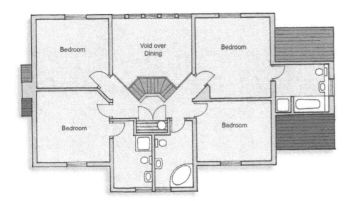

Traditional style

Floor area
225m²
2422ft²

Bedrooms
4

Bathrooms
3

Floors
2

Key features
Lobby
Dining hall
Utility
Study
Two en-suites

Garaging for
0 cars

Design
Welsh Oak Frame

www.welshoakframe.com
01686 688000

**Build cost
£202,000**

Design © Welsh Oak Frame

Contemporary style

Floor area
226m²
2433ft²

Bedrooms
4

Bathrooms
3

Floors
2

Key features
Double-height living
Open-plan receptions
Library
Office
Master bed suite

Garaging for
0 cars

Design
**Opus Architecture
and Design**

01252 861759

Build cost
£203,000

Plan no. **BHP 310950**

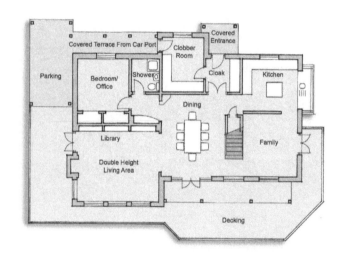

There is lots of decking outside this house and inside there's a double-height lounge, an open-plan dining room, a family room and a bay-windowed kitchen. Upstairs a gallery overlooks the lounge and leads off to three double bedrooms and a master suite.

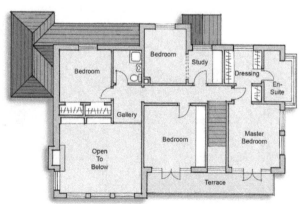

Plan no. **BHP 310107**

An octagonal kitchen and matching drawing room above create the 'wow factor' in this home. Three bedrooms, a bathroom and a study are built into the roof while the master bedroom is on the ground floor.

Traditional style

Floor area
226m²
2433ft²

Bedrooms
4

Bathrooms
2

Floors
2

Key features
Family kitchen
Dining hall
Utility room
Galleried landing
study

Garaging for
2 cars

Design
The Border Design Centre

www.borderdesign.co.uk
borderdesign@btconnect.com
01578 740218

Build cost
£203,000

Design © The Border
Design Centre

Contemporary style

Floor area

227m²

ft²

Bedrooms

4

Bathrooms

2

Floors

2

Key features
Kitchen/dining room
Gallery/study
Reflecting pool
Master en-suite
Loggia

Garaging for
2 cars

Design
Peter King

info@carden-king.co.uk
01367 253330

Build cost
£204,000

Design © Peter King

Plan no. **BHP 310230**

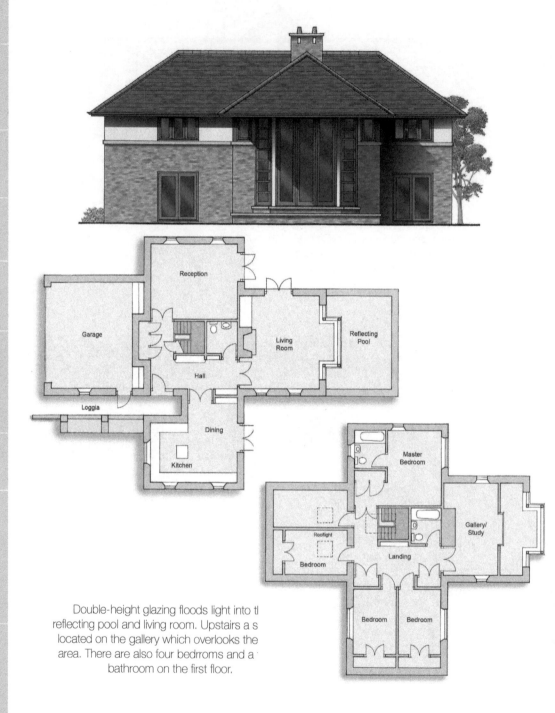

Double-height glazing floods light into tl
reflecting pool and living room. Upstairs a s
located on the gallery which overlooks the
area. There are also four bedrroms and a
bathroom on the first floor.

Plan no. **BHP 310806**

This home offers open-plan living and different areas of character and appeal. The front of the main living room, which features a large timber conservatory, leads on to a cosier living area through the galley kitchen. Upstairs there's a balconied living space, three bedrooms and a study area.

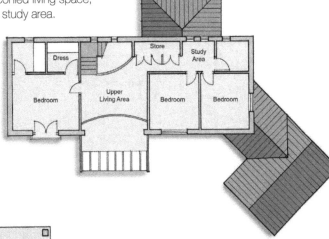

Contemporary style

Floor area
227m²
2443ft²

Bedrooms
4

Bathrooms
3

Floors
2

Key features
Open-plan living area
Car port
Upper living room
Master en-suite

Garaging for
2 cars

Design
Architecture Plus

www.architecture-plus.co.uk
01934 416416

Build cost
£202,000

Design © Architecture Plus

Contemporary style

Floor area
230m²
2476ft²

Bedrooms
4

Bathrooms
2

Floors
2

Key features
Separate dining room
Study
Reflecting pool
Utility room
Two en-suites

Garaging for
0 cars

Design
John Braid
(at Leslie R Hutt)

lhuttarchitect@btinternet.
com 01463 235566

Build cost
£206,000

Design © John Braid

Plan no. **BHP 310605**

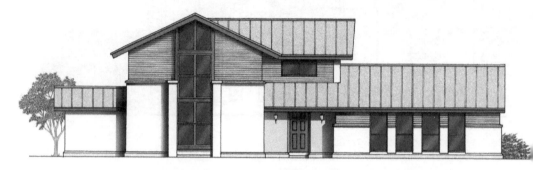

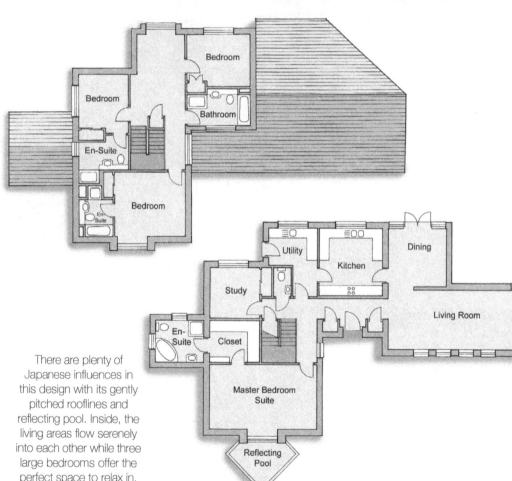

There are plenty of Japanese influences in this design with its gently pitched rooflines and reflecting pool. Inside, the living areas flow serenely into each other while three large bedrooms offer the perfect space to relax in.

Plan no. **BHP 310482**

The double-height glazed porch provides a grand entrance into this house. Other touches include folding doors between the kitchen and conservatory, a galleried sitting area and a first-floor study area.

Traditional style

Floor area
230m²
2476ft²

Bedrooms
4

Bathrooms
2

Floors
2

Key features
Living/dining room
Kitchen/family room
Conservatory
Study
Galleried sitting area

Garaging for
0 cars

Design
Design & Materials

www.designandmaterials.uk.com
enquiries@designandmaterials.
uk.com
01909 540 123

Build cost
£206,000

Design © Design &
Materials

Traditional style

Floor area

230m²

2476ft²

Bedrooms

4

Bathrooms

2

Floors

3

Key features
Kitchen/breakfast room
Separate dining room
Workshop
2nd floor playroom
Master dressing room

Garaging for
2 cars

Design
Design & Materials

www.designandmaterials.uk.com
enquiries@designandmaterials.
uk.com
01909 540 123

Build cost
£206,000

Design © Design &
Materials

Plan no. **BHP 310521**

The large porch creates a grand entrance to this three-storey home Within the double garage is masses of space for a workshop which can be accessed from the utility room.

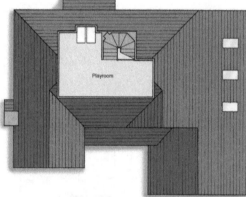

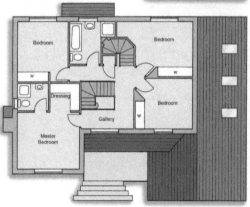

Plan no. **BHP 310716**

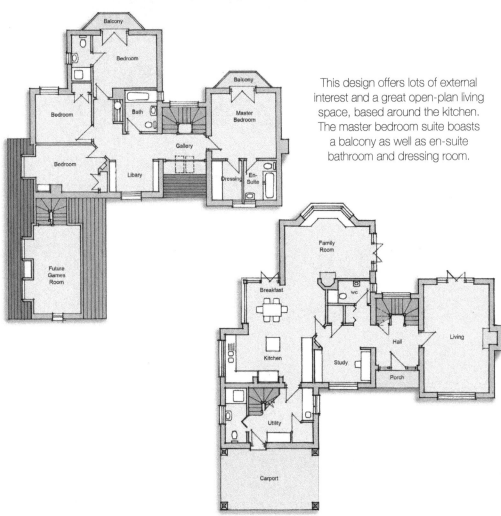

This design offers lots of external interest and a great open-plan living space, based around the kitchen. The master bedroom suite boasts a balcony as well as en-suite bathroom and dressing room.

Traditional style

Floor area
232m²
2497ft²

Bedrooms
4

Bathrooms
3

Floors
2

Key features
Family room
Kitchen/breakfast room
Games room
Library
Car port

Garaging for
0 cars

Design
Design & Materials

www.designandmaterials.uk.com
enquiries@designandmaterials.uk.com
01909 540 123

Build cost
£208,000

Traditional style

Floor area
235m²
2530ft²

Bedrooms
4

Bathrooms
5

Floors
2

Key features
Separate dining room
Study
Shower room
3 en-suites

Garaging for
0 cars

Design
Custom Homes

www.customhomes.co.uk
admin@customhomes.co.uk
01787 377388

Build cost
£211,000

Plan no. **BHP 310224**

The reception rooms radiate off a large hall which is mirrored by a large landing upistairs. The reception rooms are all separate for those who prefer a more traditional layout.

Plan no. **BHP 310932**

An unusual exterior design is matched by the interior. The dining room is accessed through the living room or kitchen. There are plenty of en-suite bathrooms – two of which are large enough to house corner baths.

Traditional style

Floor area
236m²
2540ft²

Bedrooms
4

Bathrooms
4

Floors
2

Key features
Separate dining room
Study
Galleried landing
Full-height hall
Porch

Garaging for
0 cars

Design
John Braid
(at Leslie R Hutt)

lhuttarchitect@btinternet.com
01463 235566

Build cost
£212,000

Design © John Braid

Traditional style

Floor area
237m²
2551ft²

Bedrooms
4

Bathrooms
2

Floors
2

Key features
Kitchen/breakfast room
Library/snug
Double-height hall
Galleried landing
Balcony

Garaging for
0 cars

Design
Jeremy Rawlings

www.periodhome.net
01884 266444

Build cost
£212,500

Design © Jeremy Rawlings

Plan no. **BHP 310647**

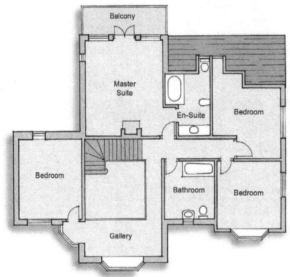

This design offers the style of a Tudor house, with its herringbone brickwork and great hall, without the angst of an older property. The ground floor is mostly open-plan which you would have with a genuine 16th century house! The galleried landing and bedroom three both have bay windows while the large master suite features its own fireplace and balcony.

Plan no. **BHP 310893**

All three rear-facing reception rooms have French doors. The library, which can be accessed from both the hall and living room, leads into a conservatory. Upstairs there is a pair of balconies for the bigger bedrooms with the master having an en-suite shower room.

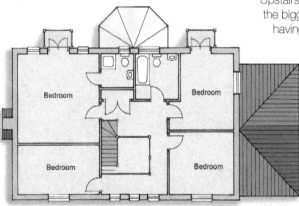

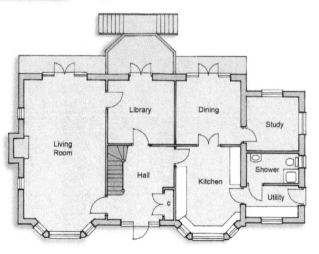

Traditional style

Floor area
238m²
2562ft²

Bedrooms
4

Bathrooms
2

Floors
2

Key features
Shower room
Separate dining room
Study
Galleried landing
Conservatory

Garaging for
0 cars

Design
Custom Homes

www.customhomes.co.uk
admin@customhomes.co.uk
01787 377388

Build cost
£213,500

Traditional style

Floor area
238m²
2562ft²

Bedrooms
4

Bathrooms
3

Floors
2

Key features
Kitchen/breakfast room
Separate dining room
Study
Utility room
Galleried landing

Garaging for
2 cars

Design
TJ Crump
Oakwrights

www.oakwrights.co.uk
enquiries@oakwrights.co.uk
01432 353353

Build cost
£213,500

Plan no. **BHP 310896**

This would make an exceptional family home with its generous size and well-thought-out layout. A dining hall forms the hub which all the ground floor rooms radiate from. Upstairs three of the bedrooms sit in the main body of the house while parents get some peace and quiet in a link-detached sleeping suite above the garage.

Plan no. **BHP 310632**

The glass-roofed family room, double-height dining hall and galleried landing provide plenty of interest while on the practical front this house also features a utility room and a bin store. The two ground floor bedrooms share a 'Jack and Jill' bathroom.

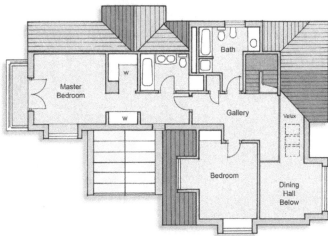

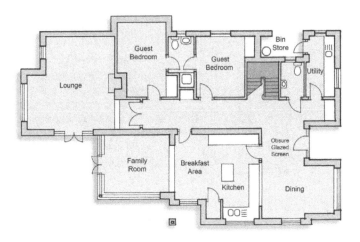

Traditional style

Floor area
238m²
2562ft²

Bedrooms
4

Bathrooms
3

Floors
2

Key features
Family room
Kitchen/breakfast room
Full-height dining hall
Galleried landing
Master en-suite

Garaging for
0 cars

Design
Design & Materials

www.designandmaterials.uk.com
enquiries@designandmaterials.
uk.com
01909 540 123

Build cost
£213,500

Design © Design &
Materials

Traditional style

Floor area
239m²
2573ft²

Bedrooms
4

Bathrooms
4

Floors
2

Key features
Kitchen/family room
Larder
Play room
Study
Living room

Garaging for
2 cars

Design
Eclipse Design

www.eclipsedesign.
copperstream.co.uk
enquiries@eclipsedesignuk.net
0845 460 4758

Build cost
£214,000

Design © Eclipse Design

Plan no. **BHP 310842**

This L-shaped house provides open-plan space for the key living areas including the kitchen/sitting room. There is also a good-sized separate living area. Upstairs the master bedroom gets a balcony, en-suite and a built-in wardrobe.

Plan no. **BHP 310788**

Traditional style

This is a luxury bungalow whose layout gives access to most of the rooms from a central corridor lit by five semi-circular windows. Also off the corridor is the design's centrepiece: an outside swimming pool.

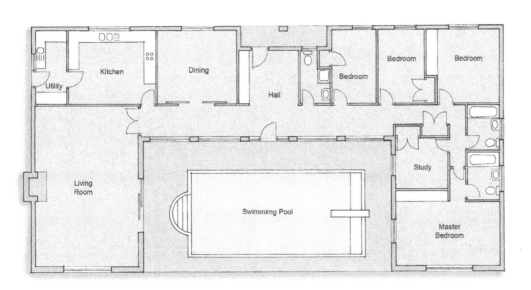

Floor area
241m²
2594ft²

Bedrooms
4

Bathrooms
3

Floors
1

Key features
Swimming pool
Study
Separate dining room
Utility room
Master en-suite

Garaging for
0 cars

Design
The Border Design Centre

www.borderdesign.co.uk
borderdesign@btconnect.com
01578 740218

Build cost
£216,000

Floor plan labels: Utility, Kitchen, Dining, Hall, Bedroom, Bedroom, Bedroom, Living Room, Swimmimg Pool, Study, Master Bedroom

Traditional style

Floor area

241m²

2594ft²

Bedrooms

4

Bathrooms

2

Floors

2

Key features
Kitchen/breakfast room
Study
Utility room
Separate dining room
Master en-suite

Garaging for
0 cars

Design
Stephen Mattick

www.mattick.co.uk
mattick@mattick.co.uk
01223 891159

Build cost
£216,000

Design © Stephen Mattick

Plan no. **BHP 310875**

This traditional looking farmhouse is full of modern features including large reception rooms, an open-plan kitchen/breakfast room and separate dining and utility rooms. Upstairs there are four bedrooms – with the master en-suite.

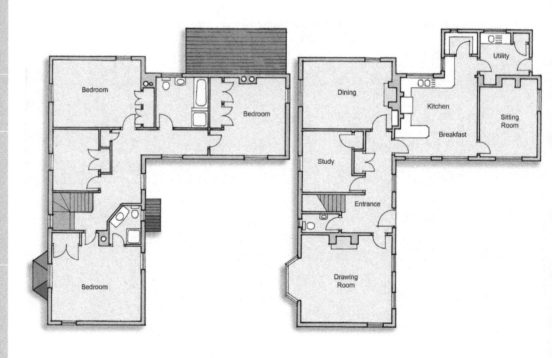

Plan no. **BHP 310323**

Plenty of external timber in ths design with its integral double garage. The gound floor features a big kitchen and living room as well as a sun room. Upstairs Velux-type rooflights provide daylight for the long access corridor.

Traditional style

Floor area
242m²
2605ft²

Bedrooms
4

Bathrooms
2

Floors
2

Key features
Sun room
Separate dining room
Kitchen/breakfast room
Utility room
Larder

Garaging for
2 cars

Design
The Border Design Centre

www.borderdesign.co.uk
borderdesign@btconnect.com
01578 740218

Build cost
£217,000

Design © The Border Design Centre

Traditional style

Floor area
243m²
2616ft²

Bedrooms
4

Bathrooms
2

Floors
2

Key features
Kitchen/dining room
Study
Utility room
Master en-suite

Garaging for
1 car

Design
Design & Materials

www.designandmaterials.uk.com
enquiries@designandmaterials.
uk.com
01909 540 123

Build cost
£218,000

Design © Design &
Materials

Plan no. **BHP** **310698**

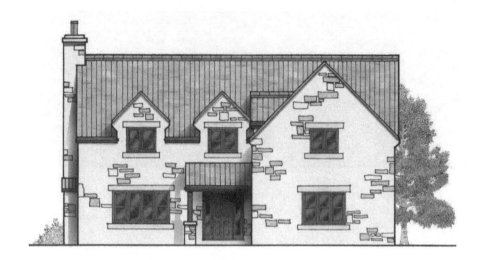

This L-shape design has a smallish hall but manages to access all of the principal reception rooms from it. Ideal if you want to maximise space. There is a kitchen/diner, a study and a utility room. Upstairs the master bedroom suite includes a dressing room and en-suite. The second bedroom has twin-aspect windows.

Plan no. **BHP 310080**

Outside you get a weatherboard and brick exterior under a tiled roof. Inside you get a kitchen with larder and utility room and a separate dining room. Upstairs two of the bedrooms are en-suite and there's a large family bathroom too.

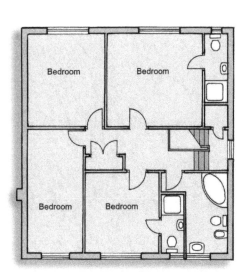

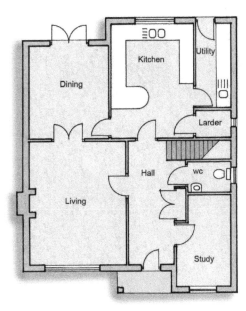

Traditional style

Floor area
245m²
2637ft²

Bedrooms
4

Bathrooms
3

Floors
2

Key features
Separate dining room
Larder
Utility room
Study
Master en-suite

Garaging for
0 cars

Design
Churchill Design

www.churchilldesign.co.uk
info@churchilldesign.co.uk
01252 325701

Build cost
£220,000

Design © Churchill Design

Contemporary style

Floor area

248m²

2669ft²

Bedrooms

4

Bathrooms

2

Floors

2

Key features
Full-height dining hall
Family room
Study
Balconied landing
Master bedroom suite

Garaging for
0 cars

Design
John Watson

Build cost
£222,500

Design © John Watson

Plan no. **BHP 310851**

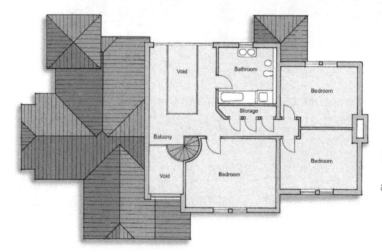

This modern take on the traditional farmhouse incorporates plenty of glass to create a bright, airy interior. Interesting architectural features include double-height rooms, a gallery and a balcony. The master bedrrom suite is particulalry luxurious.

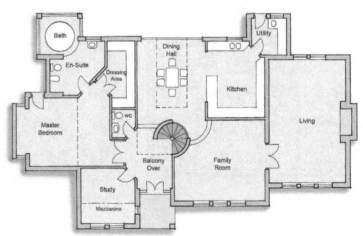

Plan no. **BHP 310128**

As traditional as this house looks from the outside the interior is designed for thoroughly modern living. That means lots of free-flowing space through the well-trod areas like the kitchen and dining room, plus a full-depth living room to relax in. The utility room is sensibly sandwiched between the main house and a garage. Sleeping space is equally generous and the galleried hall benefits from the large window on the staircase.

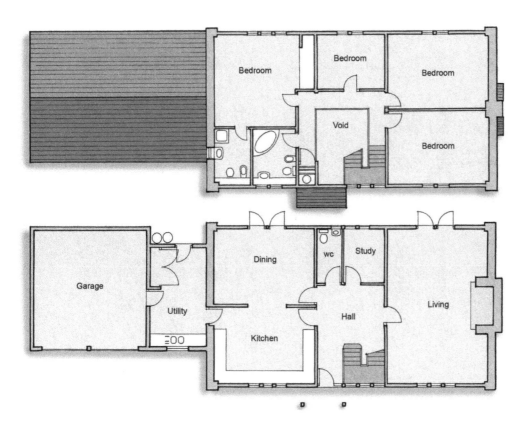

Traditional style

Floor area
248m²
2669ft²

Bedrooms
4

Bathrooms
2

Floors
2

Key features
Kitchen/dining room
Study
Utility room
Double-height hall
Galleried landing

Garaging for
2 cars

Design
Welsh Oak Frame

www.welshoakframe.com
01686 688000

Build cost
£222,500

Design © Welsh Oak Frame

Traditional style

Floor area
251m²
2702ft²

Bedrooms
4

Bathrooms
1

Floors
2

Key features
Open-plan living area
Utility room
Lobby

Garaging for
1 cars

Design
Custom Homes

www.customhomes.co.uk
admin@customhomes.co.uk
01787 377388

Build cost
£225,000

Design © Custom Homes

Plan no. **BHP 310581**

The traditional styling of this house belies a modern, open-plan interior where the hall, living room and dining room are one large space. Upstairs the four bedrooms share a single bathroom.

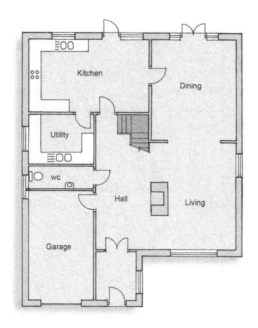

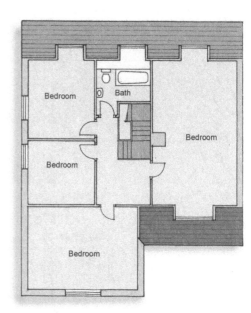

Plan no. **BHP 310884**

This Tudor-look house has plenty of flexible reception space. The sun room at the end of the house features triple-aspect French doors. There's a formal dining room close to the kitchen – which is complete with its own pantry and utility room. Off the galleried landing upstairs are four bedrooms, three bathrooms and stairs for accessing future attic rooms.

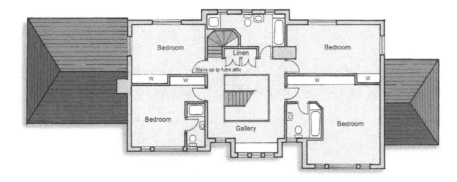

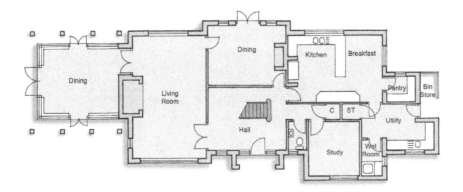

Traditional style

Floor area
254m²
2734ft²

Bedrooms
4

Bathrooms
3

Floors
2

Key features
Kitchen/breakfast room
Separate dining room
Study
Galleried landing
Sun lounge

Garaging for
0 cars

Design
Design & Materials

www.designandmaterials.uk.com
enquiries@designandmaterials.uk.com
01909 540 123

Build cost
£228,000

Design © Design & Materials

Traditional style

Floor area
255m²
2745ft²

Bedrooms
4

Bathrooms
3

Floors
2

Key features
Separate dining room
Utility room
Larder
Master en suite

Garaging for
0 cars

Design
County Contracts

countycontractsltd@
fsmail.net
01892 785153

Build cost
£229,000

Design © County Contracts

Plan no. **BHP 310986**

The kitchen is accessed through the dining room but has a utility room and larder. Upstairs the layout is more conventional and includes two bathrooms as well as a master en suite bathroom and walk-in wardrobe.

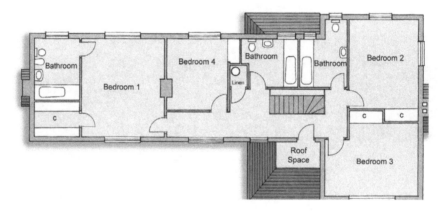

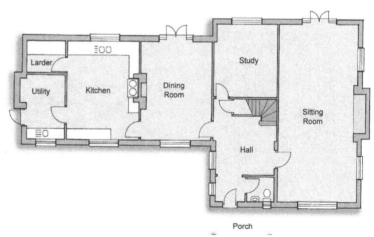

Plan no. **BHP 310236**

here is an open plan living area and the ground floor comprising hall/
kitchen and family room. Upstairs are four bedrooms — with the
master having its own dressing room.

Traditional style

Floor area
255m²
2745ft²

Bedrooms
4

Bathrooms
1

Floors
2

Key features
Kitchen/dining hall
Utility room
Study
Master dressing room

Garaging for
0 cars

Design
**TJ Crump
Oakwrights**

www.oakwrights.co.uk enquir-
ies@oakwrights.co.uk 01432
353353

Build cost
£229,000

Design © TJ Crump

Traditional style

Floor area
256m²
2756ft²

Bedrooms
4

Bathrooms
3

Floors
2

Key features
Kitchen/breakfast room
Separate dining room
Utility room
Study
2 beds en suite

Garaging for
0 cars

Design
Stephen Mattick

*

Build cost
£230,000

Plan no. **BHP**

The exterior may be period but inside there are large reception rooms, a glass-roofed kitchen, four bedrooms and two en-suites

Plan no. **BHP 310659**

Ffree-flowing space between the main reception rooms and a downstairs gym are the key ground floor features while upstairs there is a galleried landing and a large master bedroom suite with its own dressing room.

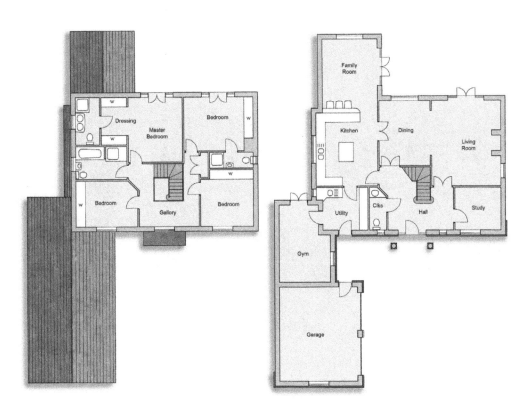

Traditional style

Floor area
262m²
2820ft²

Bedrooms
4

Bathrooms
3

Floors
2

Key features
Kitchen/family room
Living/dining room
Study
Gym
Master bedroom suite

Garaging for
2 cars

Design
Design & Materials

www.designandmaterials.uk.com
enquiries@designandmaterials.uk.com
01909 540 123

Build cost
£235,000

Design © Design & Materials

Contemporary style

Floor area
266m²
2863ft²

Bedrooms
4

Bathrooms
3

Floors
2

Key features
Open-plan living area
Utility room
Full height hall/lounge
Master bed en suite

Garaging for
0 cars

Design
Peter King

info@carden-king.co.uk
01367 253330

Build cost
£239,000

Design © Peter King

Plan no. **BHP 310746**

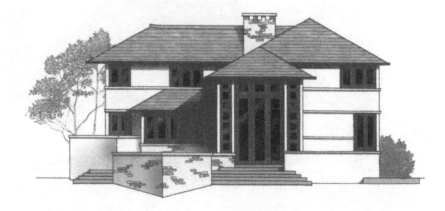

This house has flowing space inside and reflecting pools outside. The open-plan ground floor living space is a major feature. The reception rooms will fool very spacious with both the lounge and hall being two storeys high.

Plan no. **BHP 310599**

Basements are becoming increasingly popular, especially as land prices rise, and the garage/workshop space in this design add real value. The location of the utility room away from the kitchen is unusual but it offers plenty of storage space.

Boat Storage/ DIY Area

Car/Motorbike Garage

Play Room

Dining

Utility

Hall

Kitchen

Living Room

Breakfast

Bedroom

Bedroom

Closet

Gallery

Bedroom

Master Bedroom

Traditional style

Floor area
266m²
2863ft²

Bedrooms
4

Bathrooms
2

Floors
3

Key features
Kitchen/breakfast room
Playroom
Utility room
Master bedroom suite

Garaging for
2 cars

Design
John Braid
(at Leslie R Hutt)

lhuttarchitect@btinternet.com
01463 235566

Build cost
£239,000

Traditional style

Floor area
277m²
2982ft²

Bedrooms
4

Bathrooms
3

Floors
1

Key features
Conservatory
Utility room
Dining/living room
Study
2 beds en suite

Garaging for
2 cars

Design
Swedish House Co

www.swedishhouses.com
0870 770 0760

Build cost
£249,000

Design © Swedish House
Co

Plan no. **BHP 310545**

Plenty of space on one floor means a large footprint.
The living and sleeping areas are grouped together
which is often an advantage.

Plan no. **BHP 310137**

Behind the simple façade lurks a large home with sun lounge featuring a vaulted ceiling and twin aspect lounge. The first floor rooms lead off a gallery landing and include a full-depth master suite and two further bedrooms.

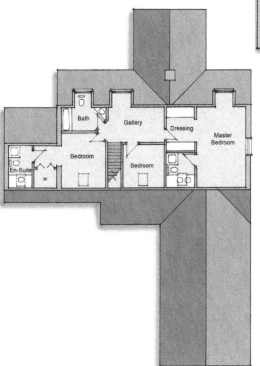

Contemporary style

Floor area

280m²

3014ft²

Bedrooms

4

Bathrooms

3

Floors

2

Key features
Open plan living
Workroom
study
Terraces
Master bed en suite

Garaging for
2 cars

Design
**John Shida
(Morningtide
Developments)**
www.morningtide.fsnet.co.uk
johnshida@morningtide.
fsnet.co.uk
01621 815485

Build cost
£251,000

Design © John Shida

Plan no. **BHP 310920**

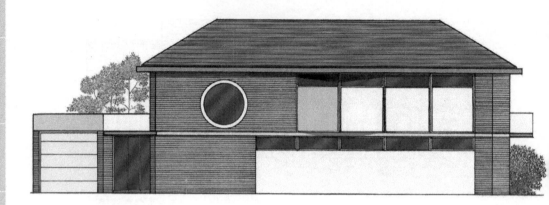

Twin terraces and a balcony would make this a good house to have orienatated to make the best of the sun. Inside, the main reception rooms flow from the central family room. Upstairs, three of the four bedrooms get an en-suite bathroom.

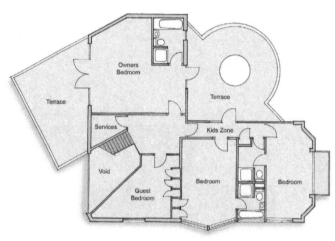

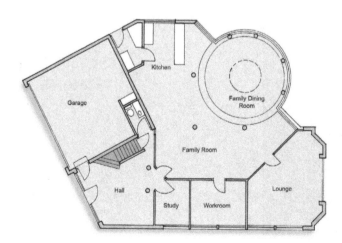

Plan no. **BHP 310074**

A two-storey conservatory links the main sections in this design and adds a surprisingly modern dimension to the Victorian-style house. The glazed area covers the breakfast room and kitchen, and provides an aerial walkway between the first-floor rooms. Dormer windows open up the roof space to provide two extra bedrooms on the second floor.

Traditional style

Floor area
287m²
3089ft²

Bedrooms
4

Bathrooms
3

Floors
3

Key features
Full-height conservatory
Cinema
Separate dining room
Utility room
2 en suite beds

Garaging for
2 cars

Design
Planahome

www.planahome.uk.com
plans@planahome.uk.com
01326 373600

Build cost
£257,000

Design © Planahome

Traditional style

Floor area
290m²
3122ft²

Bedrooms
4

Bathrooms
2

Floors
2

Key features
Separate dining room
Sunroom
Utility room
Study
Master bed en suite

Garaging for
0 cars

Design
Potton

www.potton.co.uk
contact@potton.co.uk
01767 676 400

Build cost
£258,000

Design © Potton

Plan no. **BHP 310032**

A house you can really stretch out in with enormous downstairs living areas and good-sized bedrooms above. The master is particularly spacious with its own walk-in wardrobe and en-suite facilities. The half render and brick façade combines well with subtle wood touches to give a mix of the contemporary and traditional.

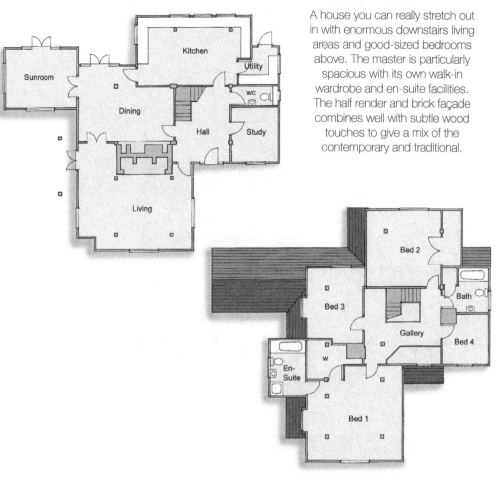

Plan no. **BHP 310977**

You can revel in the trappings of a high-end house without the need for a massive building plot. This Welsh Oak Frame design shows how with extras including a lobby, dining hall and a library all built in to a 295 square metre site.

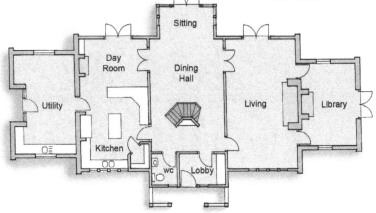

Floor area
295m²
3175ft²

Bedrooms
4

Bathrooms
3

Floors
2

Key features
Kitchen/breakfast room
Dining hall
Library
Utility room
Master bedroom suite

Garaging for
0 cars

Design
Welsh Oak Frame

www.welshoakframe.com
01686 688000

Build cost
£264,500

Design © Welsh Oak Frame

Traditional style

Floor area
295m²
3175ft²

Bedrooms
4

Bathrooms
2

Floors
2

Key features
Kitchen/dining room
Study
Utility room
Master bed suite

Garaging for
0 cars

Design
Welsh Oak Frame

www.welshoakframe.com
01686 688000

Build cost
£264,500

Design © Welsh Oak Frame

Plan no. **BHP 310017**

A double-height entrance hall and an octagonal master suite are just two of the great features of this design. Others include a separate guest bedroom, octagonal study and linked kitchen and dining rooms.

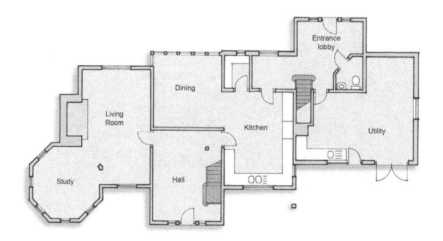

Plan no. **BHP 310242**

Find a rural plot and build your own farmhouse using this John Braid design. Inside there's all the features you'd expect like a big family kitchen and living room. Through the utility room is the large double garage – push the roof up a storey and you'd gain a guest suite or a home office.

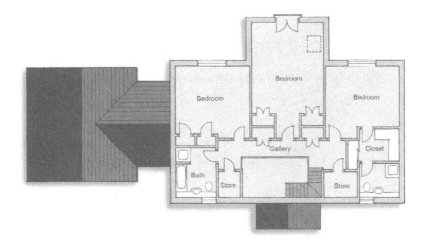

Contemporary style

Floor area
297m²
3197ft²

Bedrooms
4

Bathrooms
3

Floors
2

Key features
Kitchen/dining room
Utility room
Study
Master bedroom suite

Garaging for
2 cars

Design
John Braid
(at Leslie R Hutt)

lhuttarchitect@btinternet.com
01463 235566

Build cost
£266,000

Design © Leslie R Hutt

Contemporary style

Floor area
300m²
3229ft²

Bedrooms
4

Bathrooms
3

Floors
3

Key features
Sun lounge/conservatory
Workshop
Study
Utility room
3 en suite beds

Garaging for
2 cars

Design
JS Building
Consultancy

www.ukbuildingconsultancy.
co.uk
jsharples@ricsonline.org
0113 250 1303

Build cost
£269,000

Design © JS Building
Consultancy

Plan no. **BHP 310455**

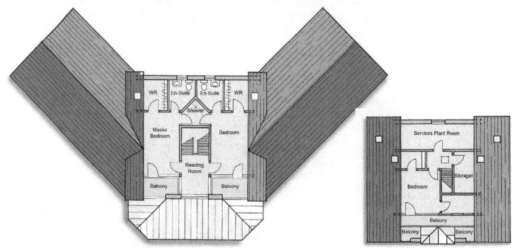

The angled wings that lead off this design's central lobby are perfect for encapsulating a perfect view or south facing aspect. The ground floor is packed with features for easy living including a large family kitchen, a dining room, a huge lounge and plenty of storage. The first floor has two bedrooms with matching balconies and en-suites. Tucked neatly into the apex of the roof is the second floor with its large balconied areas and fourth bedroom.

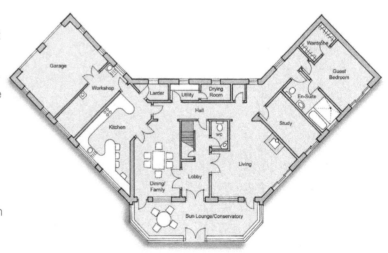

Plan no. **BHP 310554**

The part-timbering on this illustration is an attractive feature but just one of many finishes that could be employed on this Border Oak design. Build it in stone for the full-on rustic look or clad it in weatherboarding to fit in with, or stand out from, other houses near your plot. The L-shaped kitchen/den and built in conservatory are just a couple of features that make this design special.

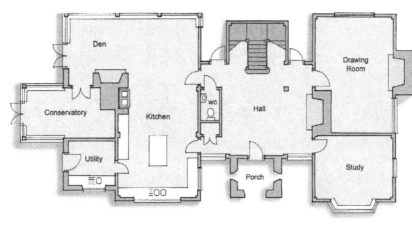

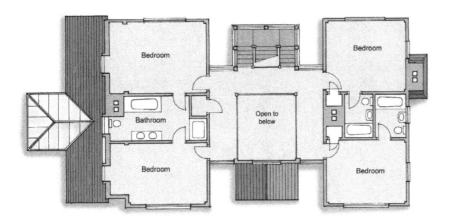

Traditional style

Floor area
300m²
3229ft²

Bedrooms
4

Bathrooms
3

Floors
2

Key features
Kitchen/dining room-
Galleried hall
Study
Utility room
Conservatory

Garaging for
0 cars

Design
Border Oak

www.borderoak.com
sales@borderoak.com
01568 708752

Build cost
£269,000

Design © Border Oak

Traditional style

Floor area
301 m²
3240 ft²

Bedrooms
4

Bathrooms
3

Floors
2

Key features
Kitchen/breakfast room
Drawing room
separate dining room
Study
2 en suite beds

Garaging for
3 cars

Design
Planahome

www.planahome.uk.com
plans@planahome.uk.com
01326 373600

Build cost
£270,000

Design © Planahome

Plan no. **BHP 310542**

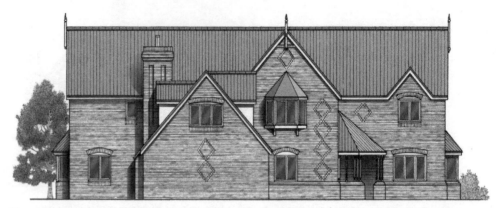

The master bedroom in this Planahome design with its terrace and dressing room really sums up the high-living standards in this house. Above the triple garage the existing plans show a third bedroom but this could easily become a self-contained office for a lucky home worker.

Plan no. **BHP 310635**

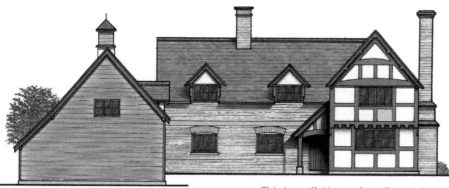

This beautiful home from Border Oak incorporates a clever layout to suit a growing family. All the reception rooms are large and have a well thought out flow between them. There's a garage and a separate store for bikes and kiddie clutter while older children could get a taste for independence in the self-contained annexe above.

Traditional style

Floor area

302m²

3251 ft²

Bedrooms

4

Bathrooms

4

Floors

2

Key features
Annexe over garage
Kitchen/diner
Study
Utility room
Master bed suite

Garaging for
2 cars

Design
Border Oak

www.borderoak.com
sales@borderoak.com
01568 708752

Build cost
£271,000

Design © Border Oak

Contemporary style

Floor area
304m²
3272ft²

Bedrooms
4

Bathrooms
3

Floors
2

Key features
Kitchen/dining room
Sun room
Twin studies
Disabled en suite
Master bed en suite

Garaging for
2 cars

Design
John Shida
(Morningtide
Developments)
www.morningtide.fsnet.co.uk
johnshida@morningtide.
fsnet.co.uk
01621 815485

Build cost
£272,500

Design © John Shida

Plan no. **BHP 310824**

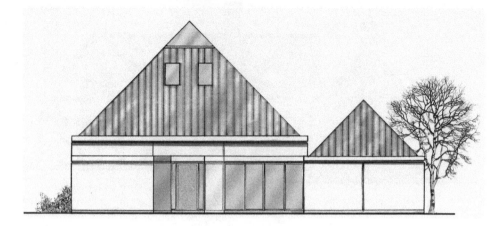

This is far more than just a design statement from John Shida, it's a superbly practical home too. There are large, smartly positioned, rooms downstairs and these combine brilliantly with the pyramid-roofed first floor and its three bedrooms and twin bathrooms.

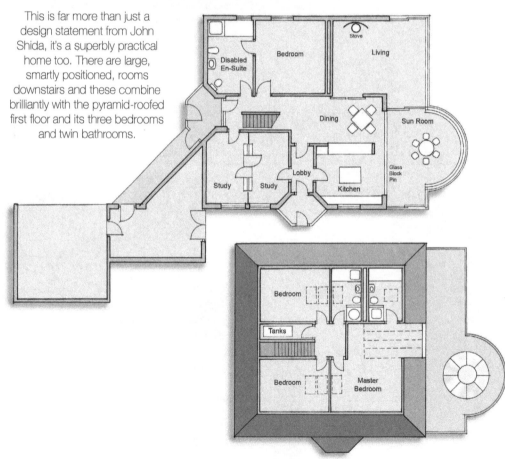

Plan no. **BHP 310995**

You enter this house through an enclosed porch that leads into a full height hall with a gallery above. Off the hall there's a series of reception/entertaining rooms and a linked kitchen, breakfast and dining space too. The first floor has four bedrooms built partly into the eaves using large dormer windows for lots of natural light.

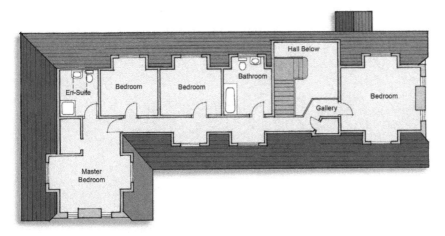

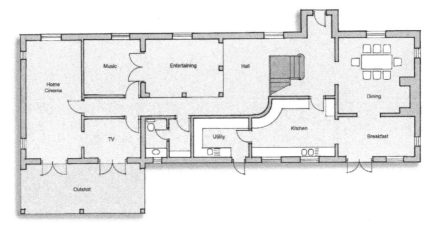

Traditional style

Floor area
306m²
3294ft²

Bedrooms
4

Bathrooms
2

Floors
2

Key features
Kitchen/breakfast room
Separate dining room
Music room
Home cinema
Master en suite

Garaging for
0 cars

Design
Jeremy Rawlings

www.periodhome.net
01884 266444

Build cost
£274,000

Design © Jeremy Rawlings

Traditional style

Floor area

307m²

3305ft²

Bedrooms

4

Bathrooms

2

Floors

2

Key features
Kitchen/dining room
Study
Conservatory
Upper sitting room
Games room

Garaging for
2 cars

Design
Design & Materials

www.designandmaterials.uk.com
enquiries@designandmaterials.
uk.com
01909 540 123

Build cost
£275,000

Plan no. **BHP 310911**

Turreted stairways, feature windows, a split-level ground floor layout
and an offset garage and games room make this Design & Materials
house an enticing layout for the adventurous housebuilder.

Plan no. **BHP 310311**

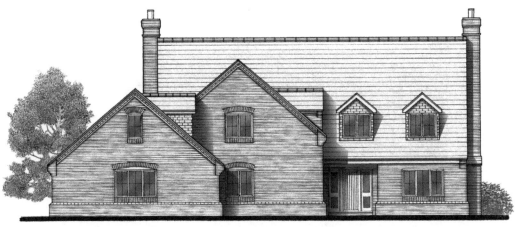

Family Room

Dining

Lounge

Oak post

Kitchen

Enterance Hall

Study

Utility

WC

Double Garage

Imagine pulling into the impressive driveway created by the front of this four-bedroom house and its twin-height double garage. Inside the wow factor continues with the large hall that's overlooked by a galleried landing. The family room is separated from the kitchen by thick oak posts and the dining room and lounge can be made into one vast room just by folding back the adjoining doors. Upstairs the three main bedrooms have generous en-suite bathrooms.

Master Bedroom

En-Suite

Bedroom 2

En-Suite

Bathroom

Open to hall below

Bedroom 4

En-Suite

Bedroom 3

Office

Traditional style

Floor area
309m^2
3326ft^2

Bedrooms
4

Bathrooms
3

Floors
2

Key features
Kitchen/family room
Lounge/dining room
Study
Office
Master bedroom suite

Garaging for
2 cars

Design
Design & Materials

www.designandmaterials.uk.com
enquiries@designandmaterials.uk.com
01909 540 123

Build cost
£277,000

Design © Design & Materials

Traditional style

Floor area

310m²
3337ft²

Bedrooms

4

Bathrooms

4

Floors

2

Key features
Kitchen/breakfast room
Garden room
Separate dining room
Study
Master bedroom suite

Garaging for
0 cars

Design
Design & Materials

www.designandmaterials.uk.com
enquiries@designandmaterials.
uk.com
01909 540 123

£

Build cost
£278,000

Design © Dessign &
Materials

Plan no. **BHP 310620**

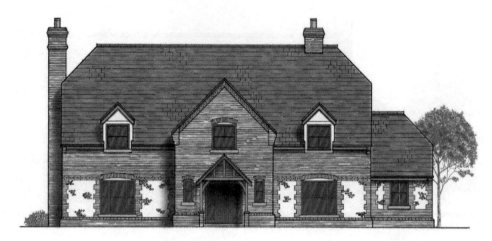

There's plenty of living and sleeping space in this treble-fronted farmhouse from Design & Materials. The large kitchen and living room have wide-open access to the garden and there's a handy utility room with a boot room attached. Upstairs the master bedroom has a vaulted ceiling, a balcony and an en-suite bathroom. Other great touches include a gallery landing, a window seat and lots of storage space.

Plan no. **BHP 310944**

Why build an ordinary house when you can put up a ranch for the same money? You'll need a big plot but just look at the benefits: there's a huge full-depth kitchen, dining hall, drawing room and conservatory on the first floor. Upstairs the master suite is at right angles to three further double bedrooms and two bathrooms.

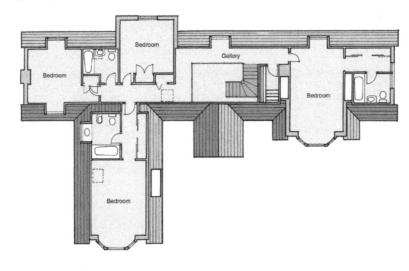

Traditional style

Floor area

311m²

3348ft²

Bedrooms

4

Bathrooms

3

Floors

2

Key features
Kitchen/family room
Separate dining room
Study
Playroom
Master bedrrom suite

Garaging for
2 cars

Design
Churchill Design

www.churchilldesign.co.uk
info@churchilldesign.co.uk
01252 325701

£

Build cost
£279,000

Design © Churchill Design

This house has large windows on every elevation to take advantage of the movement of the sun and fill the house with natural light. Inside the full-depth kitchen and family room has a built in larder and leads through to a huge sitting room and separate dining room. Upstairs there are four bedrooms and space for an extra staircase for potential attic rooms.

Plan no. **BHP 310488**

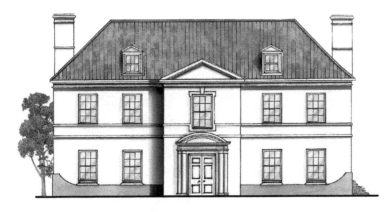

The fine symmetrical frontage of this design leads through to a less formal, but eminently practical, interior. Open-plan rooms abound downstairs while the first floor features a full-depth master suite with space for luxuries including a gym. If you need more space later on there's always the attic rooms to consider.

Traditional style

Floor area

314m²

3380ft²

Bedrooms

4

Bathrooms

4

Floors

2

Key features
Kitchen/breakfast room
Conservatory
Cinema
Study
Master bedroom suite

Garaging for
4 cars

Design
Jeremy Rawlings

www.periodhome.net
01884 266444

Build cost
£281,500

Design © Jeremy Rawlings

Traditional style

Floor area

317m²

3412ft²

Bedrooms

4

Bathrooms

4

Floors

2

Key features
Kitchen/dining room
Study
Playroom
Family room
3 en suite beds

Garaging for
0 cars

Design
Design & Materials

www.designandmaterials.uk.com
enquiries@designandmaterials.
uk.com
01909 540 123

Build cost
£284,000

Design © Design &
Materials

Plan no. **BHP 310113**

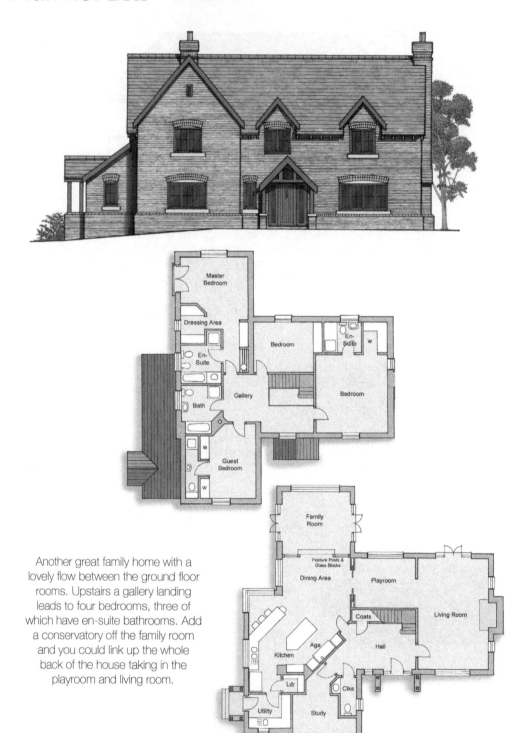

Another great family home with a
lovely flow between the ground floor
rooms. Upstairs a gallery landing
leads to four bedrooms, three of
which have en-suite bathrooms. Add
a conservatory off the family room
and you could link up the whole
back of the house taking in the
playroom and living room.

Plan no. **BHP 310602**

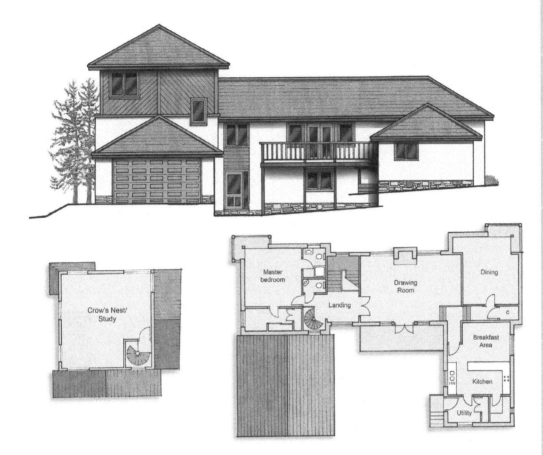

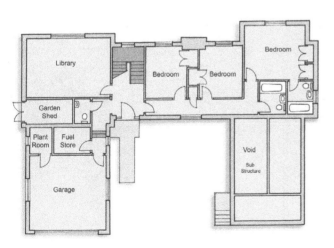

There are hints of a Tyrolean chalet in this design but you don't need to live in a ski resort to benefit from its smart layout. Inside you get three of the four bedrooms on the ground floor along with a library and an inside shed. Most of the living space is on the first floor where three of the four rooms get their own balcony. Upstairs a study in the tower above the bedroom is a handy addition.

Contemporary style

Floor area
322m²
3466ft²

Bedrooms
4

Bathrooms
3

Floors
3

Key features
Kitchen/breakfast room
Separate dining room
Library
En suite master bed
Crow's nest study

**Garaging for
2 cars**

**Design
The Border Design
Centre**

www.borderdesign.co.uk
borderdesign@btconnect.com
01578 740218

**Build cost
£289,000**

Design © The Border
Design Centre

Traditional style

Floor area

336m²

3617ft²

Bedrooms

4

Bathrooms

3

Floors

2

Key features
Annexe above the
garage and a sun
room

Garaging for
2 cars

Design
**TJ Crump
Oakwrights**

www.oakwrights.co.uk
enquiries@oakwrights.co.uk
01432 353353

Build cost
£301,000

Design © TJ Crump

Plan no. **BHP 310293**

If you have a big enough plot you could fill it admirably with this Oakwrights' design. Spreading out in three directions the ground floor features an open plan kitchen, dining hall and sunroom alongside a generous living room, store and garage. Above are five bedrooms and self-contained granny or guest suite.

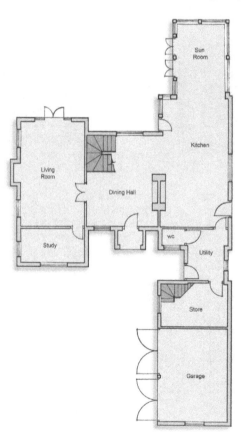

Plan no. **BHP 310470**

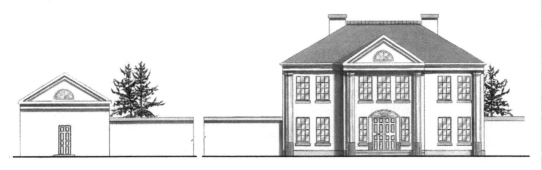

The circular entrance hall and landing in this design gives easy access to all of the ground and first floor rooms. These include an enormous, bay-fronted, lounge, symmetrical kitchen and dining spaces downstairs. Upstairs there's a delightfully decadent master suite, a gym and three more double bedrooms upstairs.

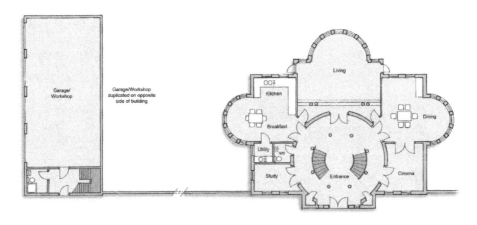

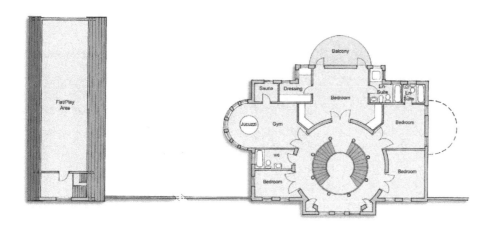

Traditional style

Floor area

340m²

3660ft²

Bedrooms

4

Bathrooms

1

Floors

2

Key features
Circular entrance hall
Kitchen/breakfast room
Cinema
Gym/Jacuzzi
Master bedroom suite

Garaging for
4 cars

Design
Centreline Solutions

---

www.centrelinesolutions.co.uk
info@centrelinesolutions.co.uk
01383 417 509

Build cost
£305,000

Design © Centreline Solutions

Barn style

Floor area
342m²
3681 ft²

Bedrooms
4

Bathrooms
2

Floors
2

Key features
Balcony and games
room

Garaging for
0 cars

Design
**TJ Crump
Oakwrights**

www.oakwrights.co.uk
enquiries@oakwrights.co.uk
01432 353353

Build cost
£307,000

Design © TJ Crump

Plan no. **BHP 310371**

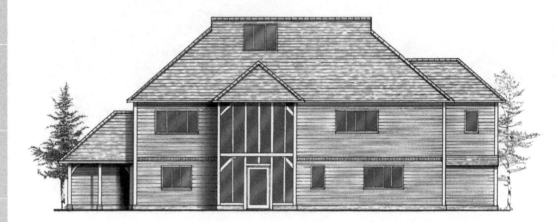

Most barns stop at the first floor, this design from Oakwrights soars a floor higher with iextra, in-the-eaves, sleeping accommodation. This frees up plenty of space on the other two floors for luxuries like a big balcony, a vast garden room and a kitchen that TV chefs would give their best apron for.

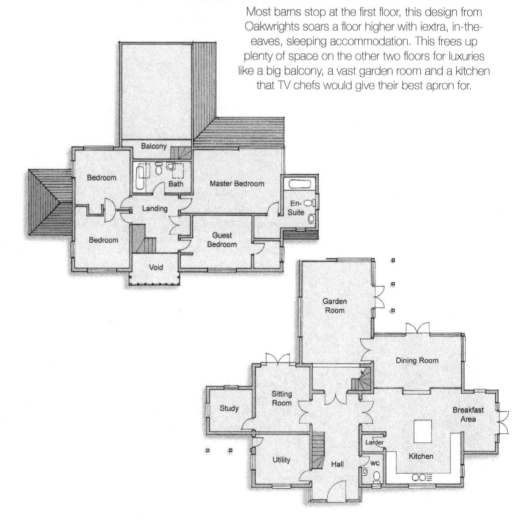

Plan no. **BHP 310434**

Traditional style

Take in that lovely old-world exterior and get ready for some architectural surprises inside. There's the basement den accessed by a spiral staircase and the roomy gallery on the first floor. Later on you could build above the garage and create a self-contained annexe ideal for granny or grumpy teenager alike.

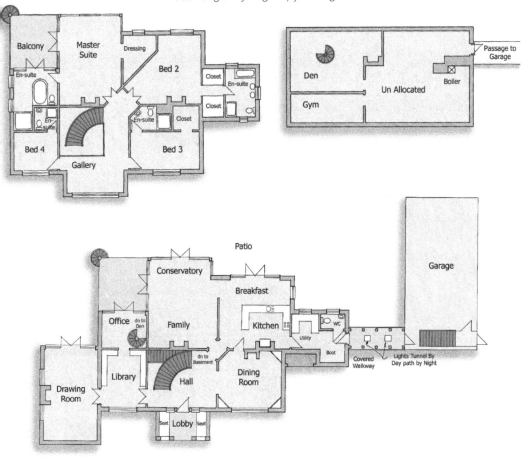

Floor area
350m²
3767ft²

Bedrooms
4

Bathrooms
3

Floors
3

Key features
Basement rooms
Kitchen/breakfast room
Library
Conservatory
Master bedroom suite

Garaging for
3 cars

Design
Jeremy Rawlings

www.periodhome.net
01884 266444

Build cost
£312,000

Design © Jeremy Rawlings

Traditional style

Floor area

352m²
3789ft²

Bedrooms

4

Bathrooms

Floors

2

Key features

Garaging for
cars

Design
Chaddock Design

www.dreamspelldesign.co.uk
info@dreamspelldesign.co.uk
01789 459148

Build cost
£316,000

Design © X

Plan no. **BHP 310047**

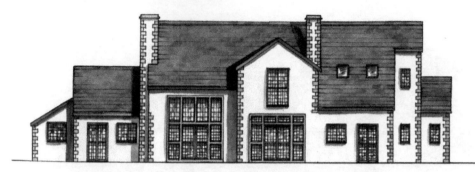

A range of different eaves heights adds interest to this design, while large amounts of glazing add lots of natural daylight. Through the cavernous hall there's a master suite and an open plan living and dining room. Upstairs the gallery landing overlooks the hall and living room before leading on to three double bedrooms.

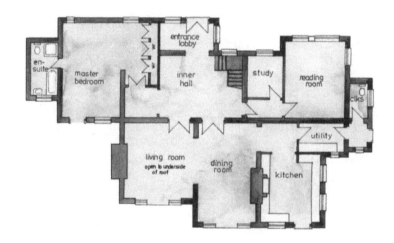

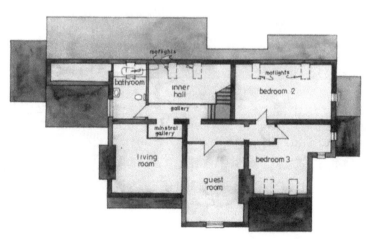

Plan no. **BHP 310170**

Traditional style

Floor area
355m²
3821ft²

Bedrooms
4

Bathrooms
2

Floors
2

Key features
Kitchen/breakfast room
Full height hall
Study
Library
Master bedroom suite

Garaging for
0 cars

Design
Welsh Oak Frame

www.welshoakframe.com
01686 688000

Build cost
£318,500

Build your own country seat with this grand design from Welsh Oak Frame. The part-timbered Tudor look outside leads into a modern home inside with luxury touches like an en-suite turret attached to the master bedroom, twin staircases and a library.

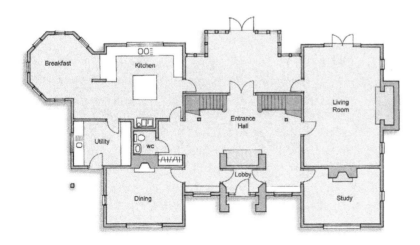

Contemporary style

Floor area

370m²
3983ft²

Bedrooms

4

Bathrooms

3

Floors

3

Key features
Spectacularly-glazed
breakfast room

Garaging for
2 cars

Design
Chaddock Design

www.dreamspelldesign.co.uk
info@dreamspelldesign.co.uk
01789 459148

Build cost
£332,000

Design © Chaddock Design

Plan no. **BHP 310728**

This handsome home offers space and versatility for the larger family. Why not use the double height breakfast room as a dining room and create a huge L-shaped, twin aspect, drawing room at the other end of the house? Downstairs the gym could become a handy spare bedroom while a suitably soundproofed music room turns into an ideal playroom for noisy kids.

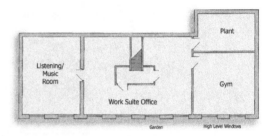

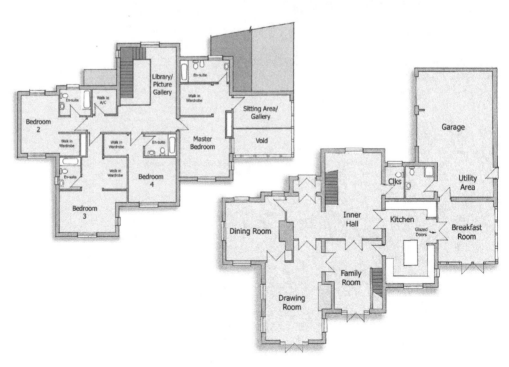

Plan no. **BHP 310827**

This is grand scale living but no space has been squandered. Just look at the neat larder and cloakroom arrangement built into the corridor from the well-proportioned kitchen. Upstairs the four bedrooms all have their own, appropriately sized, en-suite bathrooms. A laundry cupboard with a chute to the utility room beneath is a neat, and useful, touch. Moving the study upstairs into one of the bedrooms would create a self-contained home office and the option to knock the lounge into the study making a triple-lit space to relax in.

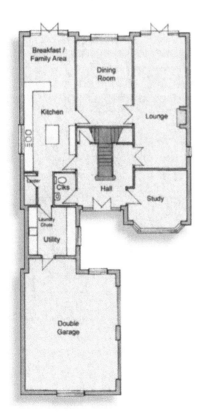

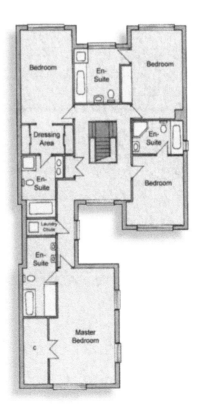

Traditional style

Floor area
379m²
4080ft²

Bedrooms
4

Bathrooms
4

Floors
2

Key features
Kitchen/breakfast room
Separate dining room
Study
Utility room
All bedrooms en suite

Garaging for
2 cars

Design
Custom Homes

www.customhomes.co.uk
admin@customhomes.co.uk
01787 377388

Build cost
£340,000

Design
© x

Traditional style

Floor area

379m²

4080ft²

Bedrooms

5

Bathrooms

5

Floors

2

Key features
Kitchen/breakfast room
Reading room
Utility room
4 en suite bedrooms

Garaging for
0 cars

Design
Jeremy Rawlings

www.periodhome.net
01884 266444

Build cost
£340,000

Plan no. **BHP 310467**

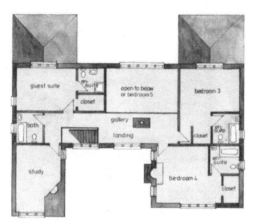

The central feature of this design is a magnificent double-height living room that sits centrally in the house. From here neat rooms, some equipped with open fires, interconnect brilliantly. The master suite takes up a decent chunk of the first floor but if you decided to position this upstairs you wouldn't be pushed for space.

Plan no. **BHP 310122**

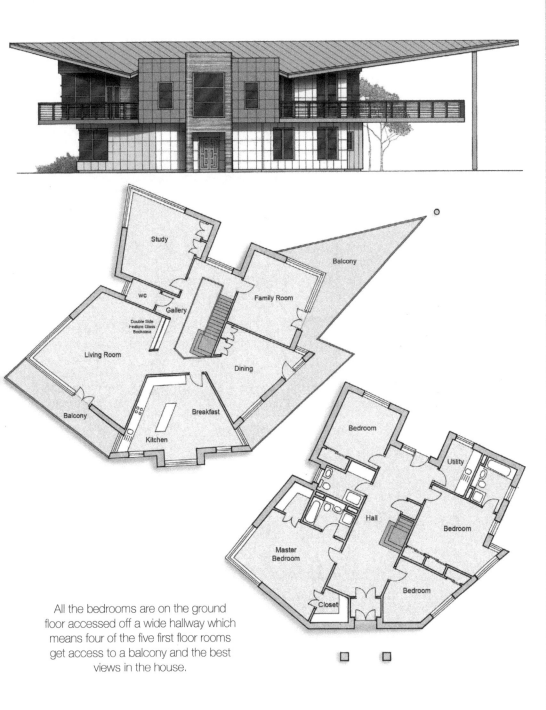

All the bedrooms are on the ground floor accessed off a wide hallway which means four of the five first floor rooms get access to a balcony and the best views in the house.

Contemporary style

Floor area
382m²
4112ft²

Bedrooms
4

Bathrooms
3

Floors
2

Key features
Kitchen/breakfast room
Family room
Study
Separate dining room
2 en suite beds

Garaging for
0cars

Design
John Braid
(at Leslie R Hutt)

lhuttarchitect@btinternet.com
01463 235566

Build cost
£342,500

Design © Leslie R Hutt

Contemporary style

Plan no. **BHP 310143**

Floor area

407m²

4381 ft²

Bedrooms

4

Bathrooms

4

Floors

2

Key features
Full-height dining room
Kitchen/breakfast room
Sun room
Family room
All bedrooms en suite

Garaging for
0 cars

Design
**John Braid
(at Leslie R Hutt)**

lhuttarchitect@btinternet.com
01463 235566

Build cost
£365,000

Design © Leslie R Hutt

Behind the ultra-
contemporary look
there's a pretty
conventional, and
ultimately flexible,
layout. Great
features include
a double-height
dining room and
hallway along
with an enormous
family room,
kitchen and dining
room combo.

Plan no. **BHP 310509**

The grand façade of this design isn't all show. Inside you get a large entrance hall and an imposing staircase to the first floor's four big bedrooms. Downstairs an archway leads off the kitchen to a dual purpose sun room/dining room.

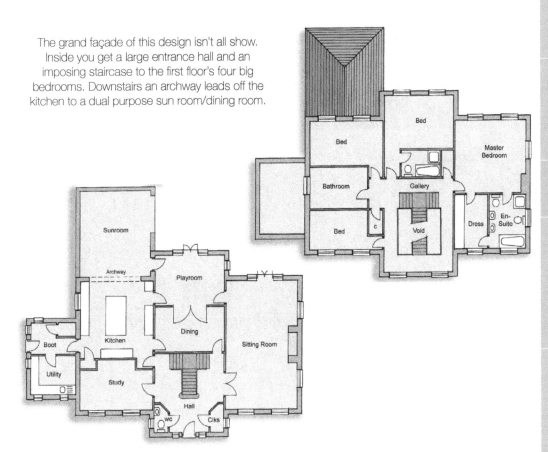

Traditional style

Floor area
467m²
5027ft²

Bedrooms
4

Bathrooms
2

Floors
3

Key features
Full-depth sitting room

Garaging for
0 cars

Design
Custom Homes

www.customhomes.co.uk
admin@customhomes.co.uk
01787 377388

Build cost
£419,000

Traditional style

Plan no. **BHP 310410**

Floor area
480m²
5167ft²

Bedrooms
4

Bathrooms
3

Floors
2

Key features
Kitchen/breakfast room
Separate dining room
Family room
Sun room
Master bedroom suite

Garaging for
0 cars

Design
Potton

www.potton.co.uk
contact@potton.co.uk
01767 676 400

Build cost
£430,500

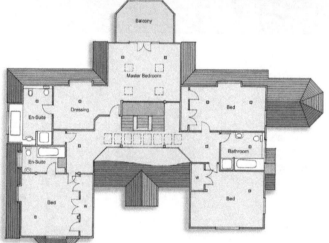

Putting just four bedrooms into nearly 500 square metres means that there's plenty of room for everyone upstairs and some great living space downstairs. Luxuries include a sun room, breakfast room and a first floor balcony.

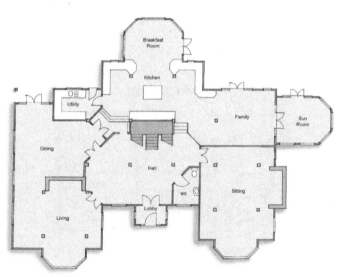

Plan no. **BHP 310179**

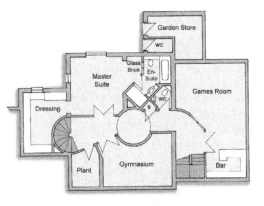

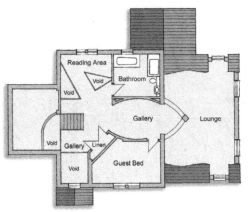

Building down as well as up gives this home some distinct space advantages over standard designs. You get room fro plenty of family and guest bedrooms, lots of living space and a master suite, gym and games room below stairs.

Traditional style

Floor area
557m²
5995ft²

Bedrooms
4

Bathrooms
3

Floors
3

Key features
Gymnasium
Family area
Games room
Dressing room
Reading area

Garaging for
0 cars

Design
John Watson

Build cost
£500,000

Contemporary style

Floor area
558m²
6006ft²

Bedrooms
4

Bathrooms
3

Floors
4

Key features
Basement pool area
Kitchen/family room
Master bedroom suite
Comservatory
Roof deck

Garaging for
0 cars

Design
Angel Design and
Development

Build cost
£500,500

Design © Angel Design

Plan no. **BHP 310257**

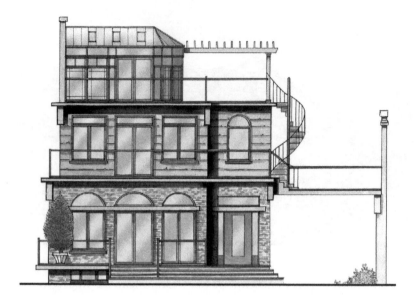

From the conservatory on the roof to the basement-level swimming pool, every floor in this townhouse is packed with exciting features. The expansive ground floor has a vast free-flowing family space arranged in unconventional shapes. The first floor features two double bedrooms, a study and a master suite with its own external staircase to the roof terrace.

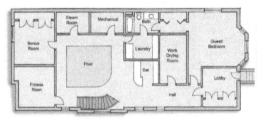

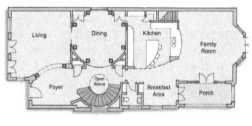

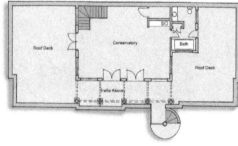

Plan no. **BHP 310011**

A basement leisure suite adds an exciting below-stairs twist to this TJ Crump manor house. When you're not in the pool or thrashing your children at table tennis in the games room you could be relaxing with a G&T on the balcony. Then there's the big kitchen and sitting room to enjoy before you take to the first floor for a well-earned rest in one of four bedrooms.

Traditional style

Floor area
619m²
6663ft²

Bedrooms
4

Bathrooms
2

Floors
3

Key features
Pool/games room
Dining hall
Study
Office
Master en suite

Garaging for
2 cars

Design
**TJ Crump
Oakwrights**

www.oakwrights.co.uk
enquiries@oakwrights.co.uk
01432 353353

Build cost
£555,000

Design © TJ Crump

Contemporary style

Floor area

140m²

1507ft²

Bedrooms

5

Bathrooms

4

Floors

5

Key features
Kitchen/dining room
Family area
Balcony
Family room
En suite master bed

Garaging for
0 cars

Design
Planahome

www.planahome.uk.com
plans@planahome.uk.com
01326 373600

Build cost
£129,000

Design © Planahome

Plan no. **BHP 310389**

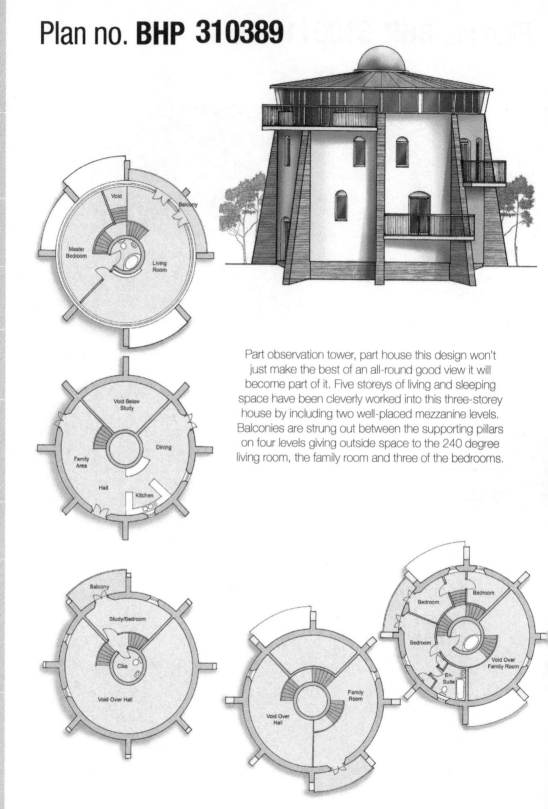

Part observation tower, part house this design won't just make the best of an all-round good view it will become part of it. Five storeys of living and sleeping space have been cleverly worked into this three-storey house by including two well-placed mezzanine levels. Balconies are strung out between the supporting pillars on four levels giving outside space to the 240 degree living room, the family room and three of the bedrooms.

Plan no. **BHP 310869**

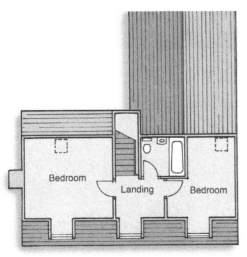

This town house design makes the most of every square metre of space to create a magnificent family home. Particularly impressive is the dormer-windowed second floor that adds two double bedrooms and a bathroom to the layout.

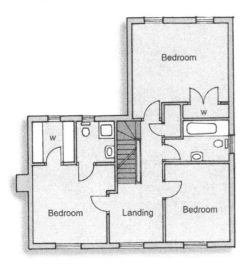

Traditional style

Floor area
152m²
1636ft²

Bedrooms
5

Bathrooms
3

Floors
3

Key features
Utility room
Master bedroom suite

Garaging for
0 cars

Design
Potton

www.potton.co.uk
contact@potton.co.uk 01767 676 400

Build cost
£140,000

Design © Potton

Traditional style

Floor area
174m²
1873ft²

Bedrooms
5

Bathrooms
3

Floors
2

Key features
Kitchen/family room
Separate dining room
Utility room
2 en suite bedrooms

**Garaging for
2 cars**

Design
**The Bespoke
Design Company**

www.planahome.uk.com
plans@planahome.uk.com
01326 373600

**Build cost
£160,000**

Plan no. **BHP 310092**

All the ground floor rooms in this design flow naturally into each other and create a great living space for a large family. Upstairs the layout provides up to five bedrooms and the clever use of space gives walk in wardrobes and en-suite bathrooms to two of these.

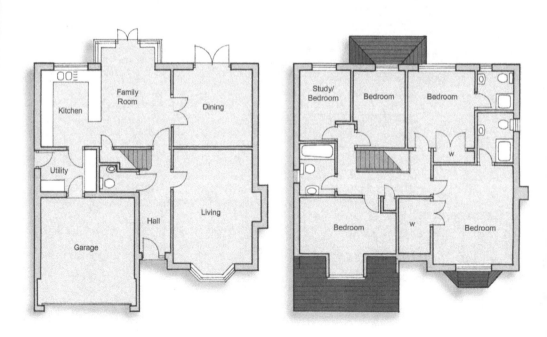

Plan no. **BHP 310536**

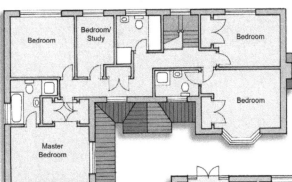

The L-shaped layout of this design creates an enormous amount of living space on the ground floor and an equally impressive layout upstairs. Highlights include an interconnected family room, kitchen and breakfast room, twin en-suites and loads of storage space.

Traditional style

Floor area
203m²
2185ft²

Bedrooms
5

Bathrooms
3

Floors
2

Key features
Kitchen/breakfast room
Family room
Utility room
2 en suite bedrooms

Garaging for
2 cars

Design
**The Bespoke
Design Company**

www.planahome.uk.com
plans@planahome.uk.com
01326 373600

Build cost
£187,000

Traditional style

Floor area
207m²
2228ft²

Bedrooms
5

Bathrooms
3

Floors
2

Key features
Kitchen/dining room
Utility room
Study
Galleried landing
Master bedroom suite

Garaging for
2 cars

Design
Custom Homes

www.customhomes.co.uk
admin@customhomes.co.uk
01787 377388

Build cost
£190,500

Design © Custom Homes

Plan no. **BHP 310176**

Building above the garage creates a gigantic master bedroom suite in this Custom Homes' design. Other smart features include a gallery landing and an open-plan kitchen/diner.

Plan no. **BHP 310158**

Brick, render and slate combine with brilliant symmetry on this Custom Homes' design. The bay windows give style and extra space to the kitchen and family room while helpful additions like a boot room and a downstairs loo make the ground floor practical too. Upstairs the two main bedrooms get their own bathrooms but bedroom three could easily accommodate a shower room if necessary.

Traditional style

Floor area
208m²
2239ft²

Bedrooms
5

Bathrooms
3

Floors
2

Key features
Kitchen/breakfast room
Utility room
Study
Family room
2 en suite bedrooms

Garaging for
0 cars

Design
Custom Homes

www.customhomes.co.uk
admin@customhomes.co.uk
01787 377388

Build cost
£191,000

Design © Custom Homes

Traditional style

Floor area
210m²
2260ft²

Bedrooms
5

Bathrooms
3

Floors
2

Key features
Kitchen/family room
Utility room
Separate dining room
family room
Master bedroom suite

Garaging for
0 cars

Design
Planahome

www.planahome.uk.com
plans@planahome.uk.com
01326 373600

Build cost
£193,000

Design © Planahome

Plan no. **BHP 310392**

Placing a gabled extension at 90 degrees to the main structure of this house means the bulky staircase doesn't encroach on the rest of the accommodation. There's also room for a study and an extra bedroom in this handy architectural add-on. Other great features include an open-plan kitchen and family room and a master bedroom suite with built-in dressing room, bathroom and sitting room.

Plan no. **BHP 310428**

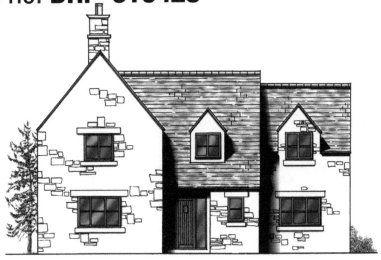

Some planning authorities will insist that you use natural stone on a new build project if it is being built in an environmentally sensitive area. This Design & Materials' house sets off natural stone brilliantly with its high, front-facing gable and stone-clad dormer windows that crop out of the roof. Inside there's a full-depth living room that spills into a conservatory and a twin-aspect master bedroom with its own en-suite bathroom.

Traditional style

Floor area
213m²
2293ft²

Bedrooms
5

Bathrooms
3

Floors
2

Key features
Kitchen/breakfast room
Living/dining room
Conservatory
En suite master bed

Garaging for
0 cars

Design
Design & Materials

www.designandmaterials.uk.com
enquiries@designandmaterials.uk.com
01909 540 123

Build cost
£196,000

Traditional style

Floor area
214m²
2303ft²

Bedrooms
5

Bathrooms
3

Floors
2

Key features
Kitchen/breakfast room
Separate dining room
Study
Utility room
Master bedroom suite

Garaging for
2 cars

Design
Stephen Mattick

www.mattick.co.uk
mattick@mattick.co.uk
01223 891159

£

Build cost
£197,000

Design © Stephen Mattick

Plan no. **BHP 310695**

This farmhouse combines traditional touches like the inglenook fireplace in the dining room with more modern ideas including the link-detached garage and a utility room. The link provides space for an extra bedroom and bathroom on the first floor.

Plan no. **BHP 310422**

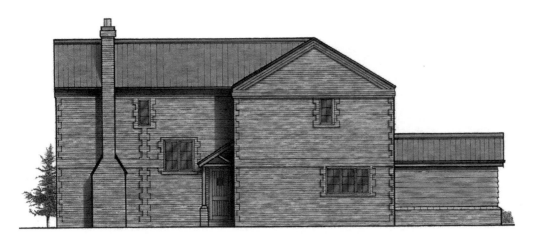

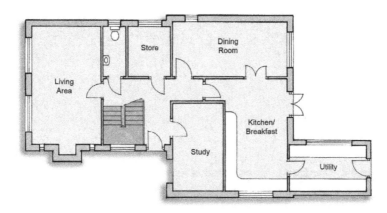

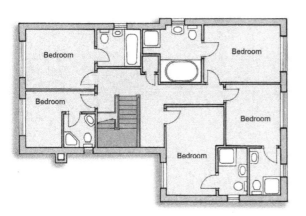

Smart design gives this house five bedrooms and five en-suite bath/shower rooms too. Downstairs a single-storey extension to the kitchen houses a handy utility room while the large store off the hall could double as a handy play room.

Traditional style

Floor area
215m²
2314ft²

Bedrooms
5

Bathrooms
5

Floors
2

Key features
Kitchen/breakfast room
Separate dining room
Study
Utility room
All bedrooms en suite

Garaging for
0 cars

Design
Custom Homes

www.customhomes.co.uk
admin@customhomes.co.uk
01787 377388

Build cost
£198,000

Design © Custom Homes

Traditional style

Floor area
223m²
2400ft²

Bedrooms
5

Bathrooms
4

Floors
3

Key features
Kitchen/breakfast room
Dining room
Study
Games room
Master en suite

Garaging for
2 cars

Design
Potton

www.potton.co.uk
contact@potton.co.uk
01767 676 400

Build cost
£200,000

Design © Potton

Plan no. **BHP 310182**

Building on three levels makes great use of a plot and creates space for two levels of sleeping space and a separate L-shaped games room. The ground floor has a full-depth living room and a dining space both with access to the garden. Add a conservatory and you've got an all-weather link between the two rooms.

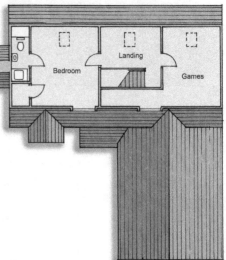

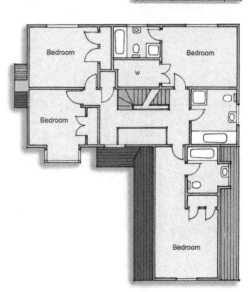

Plan no. **BHP 310719**

This grand double-fronted design has attractive brick detailing outside, twin reception rooms and five bedrooms inside. Upstairs a balcony leads off the master bedroom and the bay-fronted fourth bedroom.

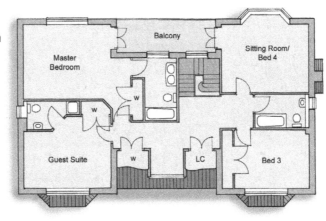

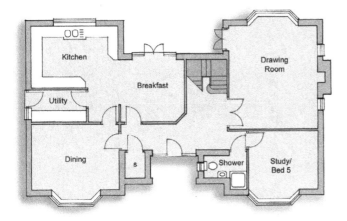

Traditional style

Floor area
235m²
2530ft²

Bedrooms
5

Bathrooms
4

Floors
2

Key features
Kitchen/breakfast room
Utility room
Separate dining room
Master bed en suite
Balcony

Garaging for
0 cars

Design
Planahome

www.planahome.uk.com
plans@planahome.uk.com
01326 373600

Build cost
£211,000

Design © Planahome

Traditional style

Floor area
240m²
2583ft²

Bedrooms
5

Bathrooms
4

Floors
2

Key features
Kitchen/family room
Dining hall
Study
Balcony
Master dressing area

Garaging for
0 cars

Design
Design & Materials

www.designandmaterials.uk.com
enquiries@designandmaterials.
uk.com
01909 540 123

Build cost
£215,000

Design © Design &
Materials

Plan no. **BHP 310947**

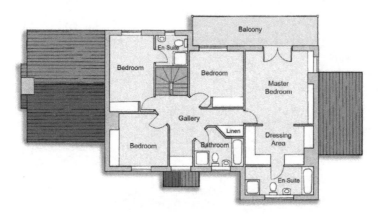

With a terrific flow between living rooms this design would suit a busy family perfectly. Among the other great features are a ground floor guest suite, four further bedrooms and the potential to move up into the loft if extra space is needed.

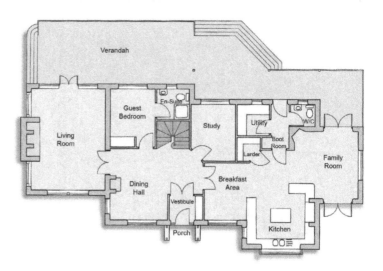

Plan no. **BHP 310962**

Wood cladding and smooth render go well together on this five-bedroom house. Inside, all the heavily-used rooms like the kitchen, breakfast and utility spaces flow into each other while the big hallway allows easy access to the family rooms and living room. Upstairs there's five bedrooms, two with en-suite facilities.

Floor area

241m²

2594ft²

Bedrooms

5

Bathrooms

3

Floors

2

Key features
Kitchen/breakfast room
Family room
Study
2 bedrooms en suite

Garaging for
0 cars

Design
Custom Homes

www.customhomes.co.uk
admin@customhomes.co.uk
01787 377388

Build cost
£216,000

Traditional style

Floor area
255m²
2745ft²

Bedrooms
4

Bathrooms
3

Floors
3

Key features
Kitchen/breakfast room
Separate dining room
Sun room
Music room
Master en suite

Garaging for
0 cars

Design
Churchill Design

www.churchilldesign.co.uk
info@churchilldesign.co.uk
01252 325701

Build cost
£229,000

Design © Churchill Design

Plan no. **BHP 310227**

Dormer windows on each elevation of this design make the best of a good all-round view and turn the second floor into a naturally lit paradise. Downstairs there are another three bedrooms and an L-shaped master suite. On the ground floor there are some lovely features including a sun lounge, a twin-aspect dining room and a combined kitchen and breakfast room.

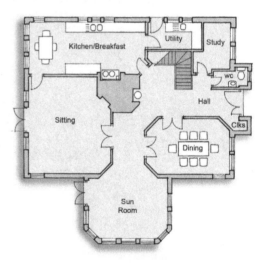

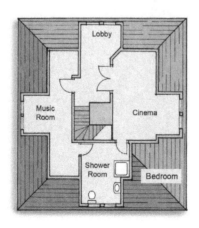

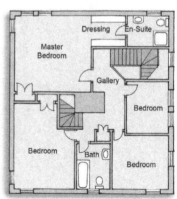

Plan no. **BHP 310983**

You can take in a great view from the first floor sunroom in this John Shida design. From the sunroom the gallery landing leads on to four bedrooms and a self-contained guest suite. Downstairs an L-shaped family and dining room flows through a ground floor equipped with two extra reception rooms and a good-sized kitchen.

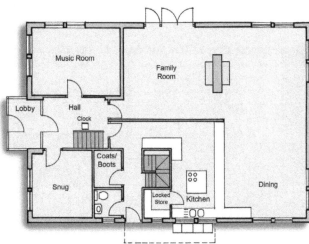

Music Room

Family Room

Lobby

Hall

Clock

Coats/ Boots

Snug

Locked Store

Kitchen

Dining

Deck

Glazed over

Study/ Bedroom

Main Bedroom

Deck Access Sun Room

Gallery

Glazed Screen

Private Deck

Jennifer's Suite

Bedroom

Guest

Study/ Bedroom

Contemporary style

Floor area
262m²
2820ft²

Bedrooms
5

Bathrooms
3

Floors
2

Key features
Open plan living
Music room
Snug
Sun room
Self-contained suite

Garaging for
0 cars

Design
**John Shida
(Morningtide
Developments)**
www.morningtide.fsnet.co.uk
johnshida@morningtide.fsnet.co.uk
01621 815485

Build cost
£235,000

Traditional style

Floor area
263m²
2831 ft²

Bedrooms
5

Bathrooms
2

Floors
2

Key features
Sitting room
Study
Separate dining room
Galleried landing
Master bed en suite

Garaging for
2 cars

Design
Architecture Plus

www.architecture-plus.co.uk
01934 416416

Build cost
£236,000

Design © Architecture Plus

Plan no. **BHP 310278**

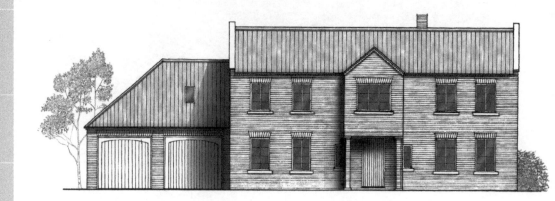

Here's a smart take on the family home from Architecture Plus. Great touches include a kids' playroom above the garage that's accessed off the kitchen – up here no one can see the mess they're making. Three big reception rooms and a study complete the ground floor package. Upstairs a bay-windowed gallery provides extra space for relaxation.

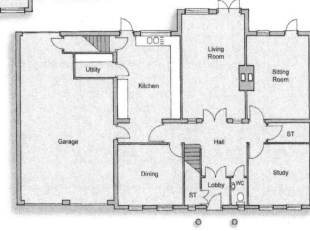

Plan no. **BHP 310077**

A very modern layout hides behind the leaded windows of this traditional design. The big kitchen is flooded with natural light from the glazed lantern in the ceiling and the French windows that open out onto an enclosed patio. The lounge also features French doors to the patio so in warmer months this outdoor space becomes an easily accessible extra room. Upstairs there are five good-sized bedrooms off a galleried landing.

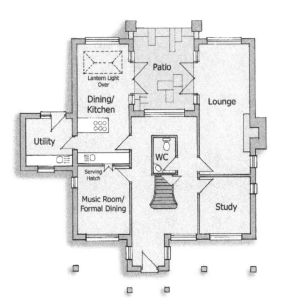

Traditional style

Floor area
270m^2
2906ft^2

Bedrooms
5

Bathrooms
2

Floors
2

Key features
Kitchen/dining room
Utility room
Study
Separate dining room
En suite master bed

Garaging for
0 cars

Design
JS Building
Consultancy

www.ukbuildingconsultancy.
co.uk jsharples@ricsonline.org
0113 250 1303

Build cost
£242,000

Design © JS Building
Consultancy

Traditional style

Floor area
272m²
2928ft²

Bedrooms
5

Bathrooms
3

Floors
2

Key features
Kitchen/family room
Study
Dining room
Utility room
2 beds en suite

Garaging for
3 cars

Design
Custom Homes

www.customhomes.co.uk
admin@customhomes.co.uk
01787 377388

Build cost
£244,000

Design © Custom Homes

Plan no. **BHP 310413**

Render and part timber on the outside gives way into a big family home on the inside. And because many families have three cars these days there's a handy triple garage linked to the house through the utility room. Create a decent-sized pitch on the garage and give it cavity walls and you could have a handy extra space to move into later on.

Plan no. **BHP 310452**

The accommodation on offer from this timber-framed house belies the view from the kerb. The secret is in the way the rear of the house extends out at 90 degrees from the main house. This section contains a generous kitchen and utility area downstairs with a large master bedroom, en-suite and family bathroom upstairs.

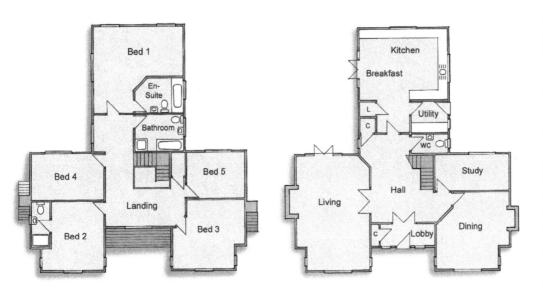

Traditional style

Floor area
273m²
2939ft²

Bedrooms
5

Bathrooms
2

Floors
2

Key features
Kitchen/breakfast room
Utility room
Study
Separate dining room
2 en suite bedrooms

Garaging for
0 cars

Design
Potton

www.potton.co.uk
contact@potton.co.uk
01767 676 400

Build cost
£245,000

Design © Potton

Traditional style

Floor area
279m²
3003ft²

Bedrooms
5

Bathrooms
3

Floors
2

Key features
Family room
2 beds en suite

Garaging for
0 cars

Design
Border Oak

www.borderoak.com
sales@borderoak.com
01568 708752

Build cost
£250,000

Design © Border Oak

Plan no. **BHP 310779**

This is a fine country barn with masses of free-flowing space on the ground floor. Upstairs the layout provides five double bedrooms, two en-suites and a big family bathroom.

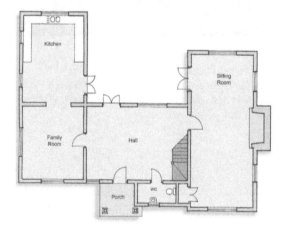

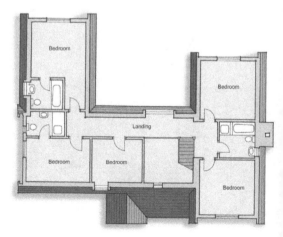

Plan no. **BHP 310131**

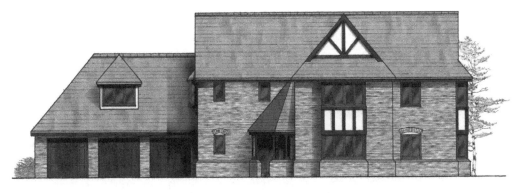

Barn-style living can be yours with this design from Planahome. Every last bit of space has been used to make a brilliant family home. And if you don't need a guest suite the space above the garage would make a perfect, self-contained, home office.

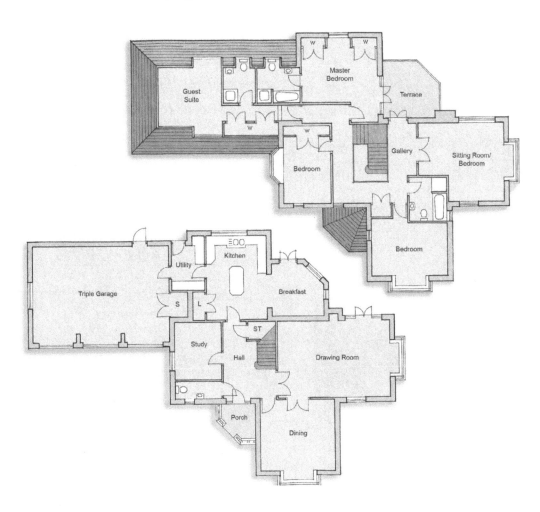

Traditional style

Floor area
281m²
3025ft²

Bedrooms
5

Bathrooms
3

Floors
2

Key features
Kitchen/breakfast room
Study
utility room
Separate dining room
2 en suite bedrooms

Garaging for
3 cars

Design
Planahome

www.planahome.uk.com
plans@planahome.uk.com
01326 373600

Build cost
£252,000

Design © Planahome

Traditional style

Floor area
284m²
3057ft²

Bedrooms
5

Bathrooms
3

Floors
3

Key features
Conservatory
Utility room
Separate dining room
Master bedroom suite

**Garaging for
2 cars**

**Design
JS Building
Consultancy**

www.ukbuildingconsultancy.
co.uk
jsharples@ricsonline.org
0113 250 1303

**Build cost
£255,000**

Design © JS Building
Consultancy

Plan no. **BHP 310665**

This design is guaranteed to make its mark on a countryside plot with its impressive, three-storey, façade. Inside the living space is large and there's an intelligent flow between rooms. If you don't need all five bedrooms the layout on the first and second floors offers the potential for a varied use of the space for hobbies and home working.

Plan no. **BHP 310722**

This grand looking house has substance as well as style. An impressive staircase lit by the feature atrium dominates the entrance hall. The lounge has a vaulted ceiling packed with Velux windows to let light flood in. The kitchen space incorporates a utility room, larder and a handy breakfast bar. Upstairs there's space for four bedrooms on the first floor and a further bedroom, playroom or studio on the second floor.

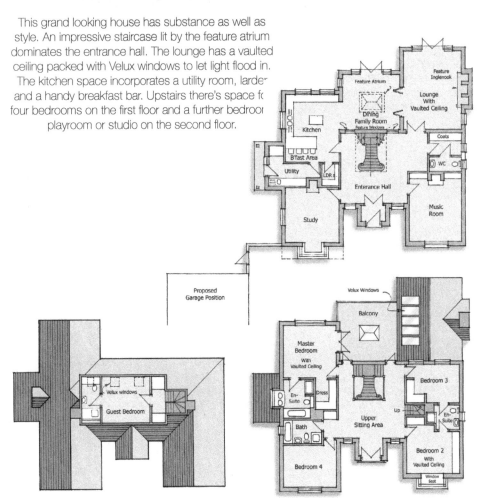

Traditional style

Floor area
290m²
3122ft²

Bedrooms
5

Bathrooms
4

Floors
3

Key features
Bedrooms with vaulted ceilings

Garaging for
0 cars

Design
Design & Materials

www.designandmaterials.uk.com
enquiries@designandmaterials.uk.com
01909 540 123

Build cost
£260,000

Design © Design & Materials

Contemporary style

Floor area

290m²

3122ft²

Bedrooms

5

Bathrooms

2

Floors

3

Key features
Kitchen/dining room
Utility room
Workshop
Study
Master bed en suite

Garaging for
2 cars

Design
**The Border Design
Centre**

www.borderdesign.co.uk
borderdesign@btconnect.com
01578 740218

Build cost
£259,000

Plan no. **BHP 310734**

This house creates its own courtyard and includes an L-shaped balcony to overlook it – ideal for drunken serenading or amateur re-enactments of Romeo and Juliet. There are four bedrooms on the first floor and a master suite on the first floor. A handy study has been included in the attic and this could easily double as a guest bedroom.

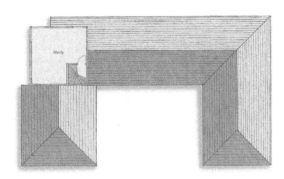

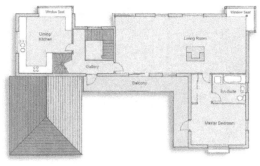

Plan no. **BHP 310902**

Timber-clad barns are the popular in the country but converting one can be a planning nightmare. Build your own though and you get to specify luxuries like a twin dressing area master bedroom, twin staircases and a vast, uncluttered, lounge/dining area.

Barn style

Floor area

293m²

3154ft²

Bedrooms

5

Bathrooms

3

Floors

2

Key features

Kitchen/breakfast room

Lounge/dining room

Utility room

Galleried sitting room

Master bedroom suite

Garaging for
2 cars

Design
Welsh Oak Frame

www.welshoakframe.com
01686 688000

Build cost
£262,000

Design © Wesh Oak Frame

Traditional style

Floor area
295m²
3175ft²

Bedrooms
5

Bathrooms
4

Floors
3

Key features
Kitchen/family room
Vaulted sitting room
Snug
Study
Vaulted master bed suite

Garaging for
2 cars

Design
Planahome

www.planahome.uk.com
plans@planahome.uk.com
01326 373600

Build cost
£264,500

Plan no. **BHP 310050**

A render, brick and wood exterior lead into a large inglenook-equipped hallway. Off the hallway the sitting room with its towering, vaulted ceiling adds to the wow factor. The first floor has three bedrooms with vaulting to the ceiling of the master suite. Guests are well catered for on the second floor with their own galleried sitting area and en-suite bathroom.

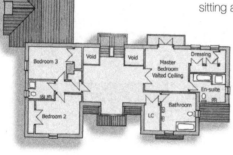

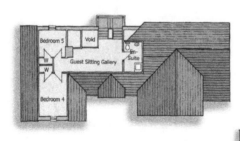

Plan no. **BHP 310953**

With its jutting gables, acres of glass and plunging rooflines this house is a superb design statement. Inside a broad hall and corridor connects all the ground floor rooms while upstairs a guest suite and five further bedrooms complete an impressive picture.

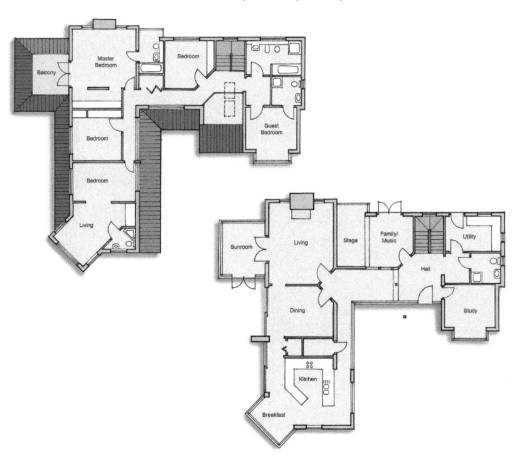

Contemporary style

Floor area
296m²
3186ft²

Bedrooms
5

Bathrooms
4

Floors
2

Key features
Kitchen/breakfast room
Family room
Study
Sunroom
3 en suite bedrooms

Garaging for
0 cars

Design
Fine Modern Homes (R.Robins)

www.finemodernhomes.co.uk
01225 777727

Build cost
£265,500

Design
© Fine Modern Homes

Traditional style

Floor area
300m²
3229ft²

Bedrooms
5

Bathrooms
3

Floors
4

Key features
Breakfast room
Dining room
Library
Basement
2 en suite beds

Garaging for
2 cars

Design
**Ian Gow
(Sierra Designs)**

www.sierradesigns.co.uk
01977 621 360

Build cost
£269,000

Plan no. **BHP 310524**

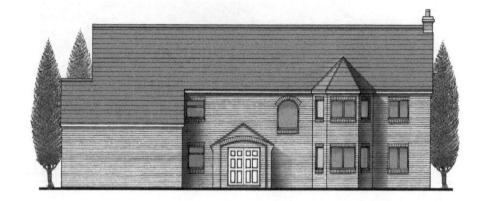

The large, well-lit, hall that gives easy access to the key living spaces matches the grand entrance to this house. The kitchen, breakfast and utility rooms are ergonomically spot on for life in a busy household. Upstairs you could move the family bathroom into bedroom three and get a large, centrally positioned, space to bathe in. This reposition would allow access to the balcony straight off the landing and extra light would flood into the space. Add a couple of roof lights and the attic rooms become instant extra bedrooms.

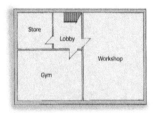

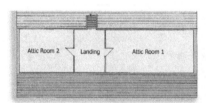

Plan no. **BHP 310296**

If you have a building plot with beautiful views, building this house will make the best of them. There's a double-balcony lounge on the first floor, a further balcony attached to the master bedroom and acres of glass on three sides of the house. If the upside-down style of living doesn't suit your needs you could split the lounge space in two and create two bedrooms with a balcony each. This would create a ground floor lounge with easy access to the garden.

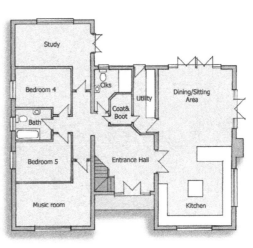

Traditional style

Floor area
300m²
3229ft²

Bedrooms
5

Bathrooms
3

Floors
2

Key features
Kitchen/dining room
Utilty room
Study
Music room
Master bedroom suite

Garaging for
0 cars

Design
Churchill Design

www.churchilldesign.co.uk
info@churchilldesign.co.uk
01252 325701

Build cost
£269,000

Design © Churchill Design

Contemporary style

Floor area
300m²
3229ft²

Bedrooms
5

Bathrooms
3

Floors
2

Key features
Kitchen/breakfast room
Dining room
Family room
Study
2 en suite beds

Garaging for
2 cars

Design
Design & Materials

www.designandmaterials.uk.com
enquiries@designandmaterials.uk.com
01909 540 123

Build cost
£269,000

Plan no. **BHP 310332**

It will take a big plot, but just look at what you'd get if you were to build this Design & Materials' house. Downstairs there's more than a hint of luxury living with the glass-roofed garden room that leads directly off the large family room. If you needed more space there's always the loft and the pitched roof above the garage would make a great office.

Plan no. **BHP 310206**

Designed in a H-pattern this house keeps the relaxing area of the sitting room well apart from the large kitchen. You could bridge the gap a little by using part of the hall space as a dining area. Upstairs, warring factions of brothers and sisters can be separated by the landing area that also houses the family bathroom – an ideal spot for an uneasy truce.

Traditional style

Floor area
302m²
3251ft²

Bedrooms
5

Bathrooms
3

Floors
2

Key features
Kitchen/dining room
Utility room
Galleried landing
2 en suite bedrroms

Garaging for
0 cars

Design
Border Oak

www.borderoak.com
sales@borderoak.com
01568 708752

Build cost
£271,000

Design © Border Oak

Traditional style

Floor area
305m^2
3283ft^2

Bedrooms
5

Bathrooms
3

Floors
2

Key features
Open plan living area
Living room
Utility room
Galleried landing
2 en suite beds

Garaging for
0 cars

Design
Welsh Oak Frame

www.welshoakframe.com
01686 688000

Build cost
£273,500

Design © Welsh Oak Frame

Plan no. **BHP 310923**

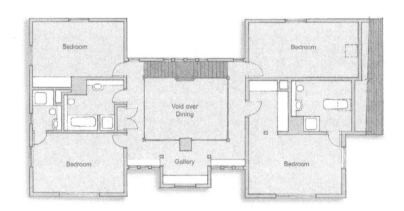

Plan no. **BHP 310140**

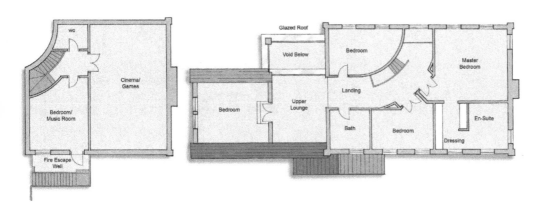

Traditional style

Floor area
310m²
3337ft²

Bedrooms
5

Bathrooms
2

Floors
3

Key features
Family room
Study
Utility room
Cinema/games room
Master bed en suite

Garaging for
2 cars

Design
John Watson

Build cost
£278,000

Design © John Watson

Traditional style

Floor area

310m²

3337ft²

Bedrooms

5

Bathrooms

3

Floors

2

Key features
Kitchen/breakfast room
Utility room
Two studies
TV room
2 en suite beds

Garaging for
0 cars

Design

Build cost

Design © Potton

Plan no. **BHP 320651**

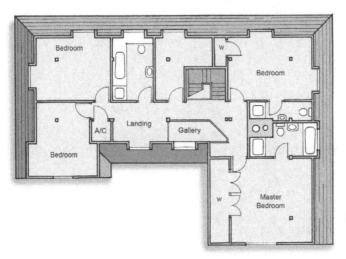

This large family home from Potton packs plenty of glass into its handsome façade providing well-lit rooms all day long. Inside the kitchen and dining room take up the full depth of the house, and if you need more space for eating you could break through the wall of the adjacent study (one of two in the ground floor). Upstairs there are four double bedrooms, one single, three bathrooms and a gallery landing that overlooks the hall.

Plan no. **BHP 310926**

Using natural stone sparingly on an otherwise rendered façade creates a great feature, but keeps build costs down, on this triple-fronted house. Inside smart touches include the family and dining rooms linked by a conservatory and an upstairs sitting area on the gallery landing.

Homebuilding & Renovating Book of House Plans 281

Traditional style

Floor area
317m²
3412ft²

Bedrooms
5

Bathrooms
3

Floors
2

Key features
Kitchen/breakfast room
Conservatory
Family room
Study
2 en suite bedrooms

Garaging for
0 cars

Design
Design & Materials

www.designandmaterials.uk.com
enquiries@designandmaterials.uk.com
01909 540 123

Build cost
£284,000

Design © Design & Materials

Contemporary style

Floor area
320m²
3444ft²

Bedrooms
5

Bathrooms
4

Floors
2

Key features
Kitchen/dining room
Studio
Spiral staircase
4 beds en suite

Garaging for
0 cars

Design
**John Shida
(Morningtide
Developments)**
www.morningtide.fsnet.co.uk
johnshida@morningtide.
fsnet.co.uk
01621 815485

Build cost
£287,000

Design © John Shida

Plan no. **BHP 310023**

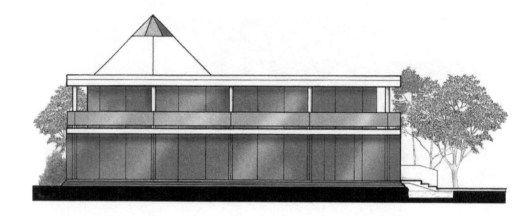

A fully-glazed elevation on one side of this house makes the most of a great view while lightweight insulated panel construction elsewhere helps it comply with energy conservation rules. Inside an open-plan layout lets the light wash through the rooms on both floors and the main bedroom even gets a view of the sky thanks to its glass-topped feature roof.

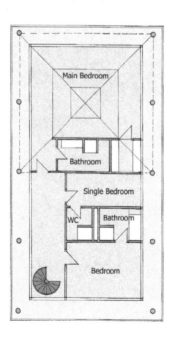

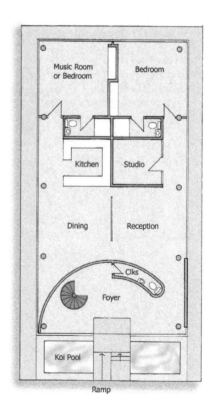

Plan no. **BHP 310689**

This double-fronted house has real kerb appeal thanks to its part timbered and brick finish. Inside the hall leads straight through to a large kitchen past a living room, dining room and study. The living room could be sectioned off to make a dining space closer to the kitchen and the existing dining room could turn into a playroom or even a guest suite.

Traditional style

Floor area
321m²
3455ft²

Bedrooms
5

Bathrooms
2

Floors
2

Key features
Kitchen/breakfast room
Separate dining room
Utility room
Study
2 en suite bedrooms

Garaging for
0 cars

Design
Potton

www.potton.co.uk
contact@potton.co.uk
01767 676 400

Build cost
£288,000

Design © Potton

Traditional style

Floor area
325m²
3498ft²

Bedrooms
5

Bathrooms
3

Floors
2

Key features
Kitchen/breakfast room
Full height lounge
Reading room
Study
2 en suite bedrooms

Garaging for
0 cars

Design
Design & Materials

www.designandmaterials.uk.com
enquiries@designandmaterials.
uk.com
01909 540 123

Build cost
£291,000

Design © X

Plan no. **BHP 310878**

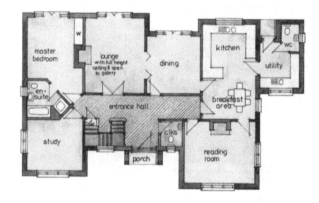

This traditional-looking design would sit perfectly on a rural plot and, if you specified the local stone, it would look like it has always been there. Inside there are three big reception rooms on the first floor along with a good-sized kitchen and breakfast area. The first floor features a gallery landing over the lounge, a sitting room, guest suite and three bedrooms.

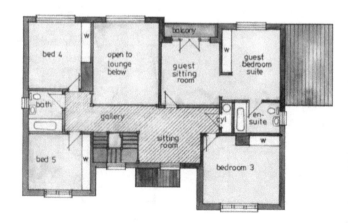

Plan no. **BHP 310308**

Traditional style

If your plot has got great views you can make the most of them with this design – the large windows on every elevation see to that. Inside that part-timbered exterior lies a wonderful layout of rooms including five bedrooms, a separate TV room and twin studies.

Floor area
327m²
3520ft²

Bedrooms
5

Bathrooms
4

Floors
2

Key features
Kitchen/dining room
Utility room
TV room
2 studies
2 en suite bedrooms

Garaging for
0 cars

Design
Potton

www.potton.co.uk
contact@potton.co.uk
01767 676 400

Build cost
£293,000

Design © Potton

Contemporary style

Floor area
334m²
3595ft²

Bedrooms
5

Bathrooms
3

Floors
2

Exceptional features
Kitchen/breakfast room
Full height lounge
Study
Family room
Master bedrrom suite

Garaging for
2 cars

Design
Design & Materials

www.designandmaterials.uk.com
enquiries@designandmaterials.
uk.com
01909 540 123

Build cost
£299,500

Plan no. **BHP 310629**

This beautiful family home has a wow factor at almost every turn. There's an impressive heavily-glazed façade, a double-height 'cathedral' lounge and a multi-aspect sun lounge. On the practical front there's a vast kitchen and breakfast area with an adjoining family room. Upstairs the gallery landing overlooks the lounge and the hallway giving a terrific feeling of space.

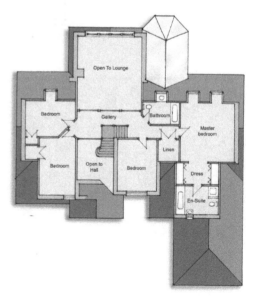

Plan no. **BHP 310890**

This uncluttered double-fronted design features three floors of living and sleeping space. The ground floor includes an integral sun lounge and open-plan kitchen and breakfast area and up to four further reception rooms. Off the galleried landing on the first floor there's five bedrooms and stairs to a useful attic space.

Traditional style

Floor area

335m²

3606ft²

Bedrooms

5

Bathrooms

3

Floors

3

Key features
Kitchen/breakfast room
Sun lounge
Family room
Separate dining room
All bedrooms en suite

Garaging for
2 cars

Design
Design & Materials

www.designandmaterials.uk.com
enquiries@designandmaterials.
uk.com
01909 540 123

Build cost
£300,000

Design © Design &
Materials

Traditional style

Floor area

340m²

3660ft²

Bedrooms

5

Bathrooms

4

Floors

2

Key features
Grand entrance hall
Cinema
Kitchen/breakfast room
Conservatory
Gym

Garaging for
4 cars

Design
Design & Materials

www.designandmaterials.uk.com
enquiries@designandmaterials.
uk.com
01909 540 123

Build cost
£305,000

Plan no. **BHP 310917**

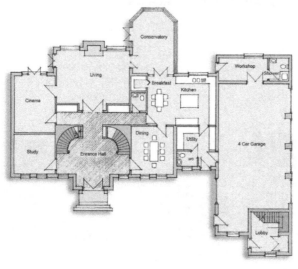

Twin sweeping staircases in a double height entrance hall set the scene for this impressive house. Beyond the entrance hall the rooms are well laid out with a free flow between the kitchen, breakfast room and bay-fronted conservatory. The first floor rooms radiate out from galleried landing and include a master suite with balcony and space for a gym. There's a separate flight of stairs up to a self-contained annexe – ideal for granny or visiting relatives.

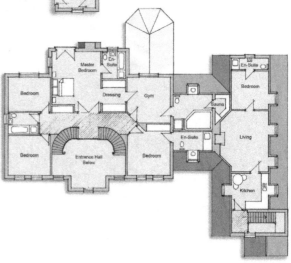

Plan no. **BHP 310008**

A balconied master bedroom up to six extra bedrooms and a double height, expansively glazed, sun lounge makes this a study in luxury living. The upper sitting area could double as an occasional office space to take advantage of the light flooding through. Keen gardeners may want to consider making the ground floor shower accessible from the garage to keep the filth of the outdoors away from that beautiful interior.

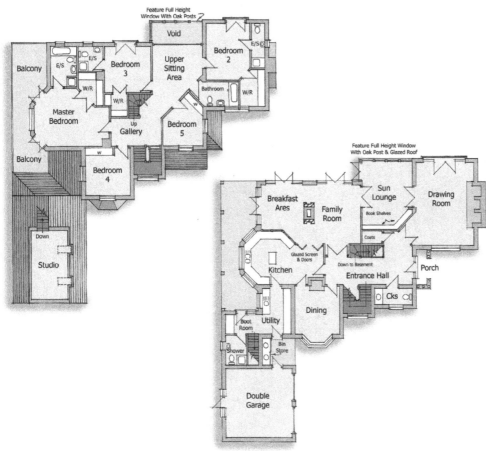

Traditional style

Floor area
345m²
3714ft²

Bedrooms
5

Bathrooms
5

Floors
2

Key features
Kitchen/family room
Sun lounge
Studio
Separate dining room
3 bedrooms en suite

**Garaging for
2 cars**

**Design
Design & Materials**

www.designandmaterials.uk.com
enquiries@designandmaterials.uk.com
01909 540 123

**Build cost
£309,500**

Contemporary style

Floor area
347m²
3735ft²

Bedrooms
5

Bathrooms
3

Floors
4

Key features
Basement gym
Study
Vaulted family room
Utility room
Vaulted master suite

Garaging for
2 cars

Design
Design & Materials

www.designandmaterials.uk.com
enquiries@designandmaterials.
uk.com
01909 540 123

Build cost
£311,000

Design © Daeign &
Materials

Plan no. **BHP 310701**

This design would make the best possible use of a long narrow plot. There are plenty of features to excite including vaulted ceilings in the family room, master bedroom and second bedroom. A vestibule, a gallery and an underground gym add to the intrigue.

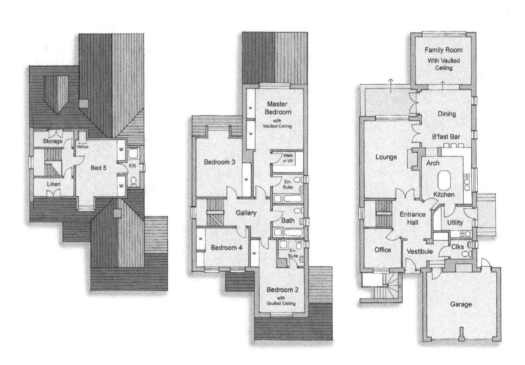

Plan no. **BHP 310290**

If you looking for a low roofline and dormer windows then this house could be ideal. Downstairs accommodation is generous while the design of the roof allows for a neat balcony off the upstairs sitting area.

Traditional style

Floor area
344m²
3703ft²

Bedrooms
5

Bathrooms
3

Floors
2

Key features
Kitchen/breakfast room
Family room
Snooker room
Separate dining room
2 bedrroms en suite

**Garaging for
2 cars**

**Design
John Braid
(at Leslie R Hutt)**

lhuttarchitect@btinternet.com
01463 235566

£

**Build cost
£308,500**

Design © Leslie R Hutt

Plan no. **BHP 310776**

This is a deceptively spacious house that makes excellent use of a relatively low roof height and dormer windows. You could consider removing the wall between the breakfast area to create a vast, triple-aspect, living space downstairs. Upstairs the layout is superb with a balcony off the main bedroom, two further bedrooms and a study. Adding some Velux-type windows above the end bedroom could create some dramatic lighting effects throughout the day.

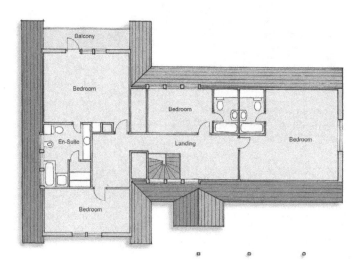

Plan no. **BHP 310527**

The lines of this classical house, with stucco walls framed by stone quoins give away no secrets of the open plan, easy flowing interior. You enter through the galleried hallway into a world of space and opulence crowned by a full-width conservatory at the rear of the house. The first floor is just as impressive with its central master suite, balcony and four double bedrooms.

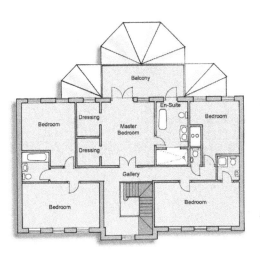

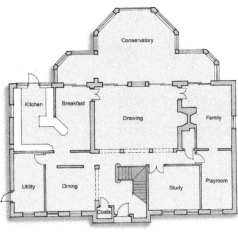

Traditional style

Floor area
364m²
3918ft²

Bedrooms
5

Bathrooms
3

Floors
2

Key features
Conservatory
Kitchen/breakfast room
Family room
Playroom
2 en suite beds

Garaging for
0 cars

Design
Jeremy Rawlings

www.periodhome.net
01884 266444

Build cost
£326,500

Traditional style

Floor area
380m²
4090ft²

Bedrooms
5

Bathrooms
3

Floors
2

Key features
Separate dining room
Reading room
2 en suite bedrooms

Garaging for
2 cars

Design
ICD Dzine

www.icd-dzine.com
01638 610117

Build cost
£341,000

Design © X

Plan no. **BHP 310500**

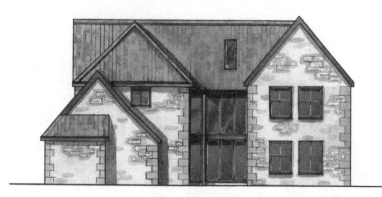

The formal layout in this design provides space for four large rooms and a full-width lounge on the ground floor. Upstairs four equal-sized bedrooms, one with en-suite are accessed from a landing and a bridge that overlooks the lounge space.

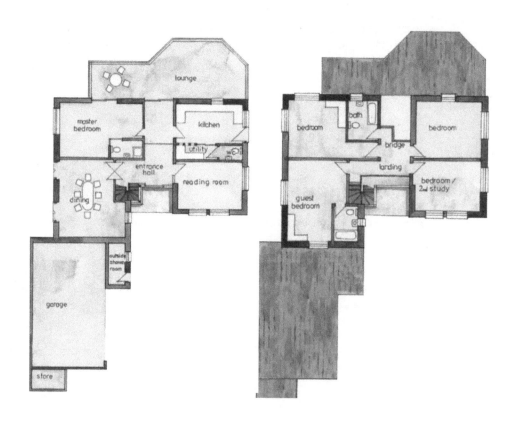

Plan no. **BHP 310437**

Taking the double-fronted concept to the extreme is this design in luxury by Potton. Inside oak pillars abound in the spacious ground floor rooms that lead onto an enormous indoor pool. Vaulted ceilings are key features in the front bedrooms while a large balcony leads off the two rear bedrooms. Luxury indeed.

Traditional style

Floor area
383m²
4123ft²

Bedrooms
5

Bathrooms
3

Floors
2

Key features
Indoor swimming pool
Family room
Separate diniing room
Galleried landing
2 en suite bedrooms

Garaging for
0 cars

Design
Potton

www.potton.co.uk
contact@potton.co.uk
01767 676 400

Build cost
£343,500

Design © Potton

Traditional style

Floor area
390m²
4198ft²

Bedrooms
6

Bathrooms
5

Floors
2

Key features
Kitchen/living room
Granny annexe
Bedsit over garage
2 en suite beds

Garaging for
2 cars

Design
Design & Materials

www.designandmaterials.uk.com
enquiries@designandmaterials.
uk.com
01909 540 123

Build cost
£350,000

Design © Design &
Materials

Plan no. **BHP 310578**

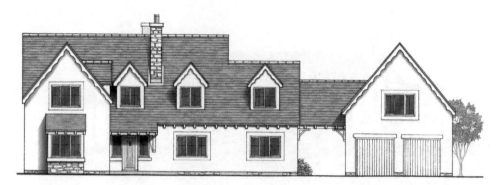

The superbly functional design provides five bedrooms in the main house and a self-contained annexe above the garage. Other nice touches include a master bedroom that looks out over the impressive courtyard and a galleried landing upstairs.

Plan no. **BHP 310254**

For those with a big enough plot this house offers the look of a 'small country estate' with plenty of features and an indication of where to put the swimming pool!

Traditional style

Floor area
399m²
4295ft²

Bedrooms
5

Bathrooms
4

Floors
2

Key features
Kitchen/family room
Snooker room
separate dining room
Conservatory
3 en suite bedrooms

Garaging for 3 cars

Design
Planahome

www.planahome.uk.com
plans@planahome.uk.com
01326 373600

Build cost £358,000

Design
© Planahome

Traditional style

Floor area
400m²
4306ft²

Bedrooms
5

Bathrooms
5

Floors
2

Key features
Kitchen/breakfast
room
Sparate dining room
Family room
4 beds en suite

Garaging for
0 cars

Design
John Braid
(at Leslie R Hutt)

lhuttarchitect@btinternet.com
01463 235566

Build cost
£359,000

Design © Leslie R Hutt

Plan no. **BHP 310317**

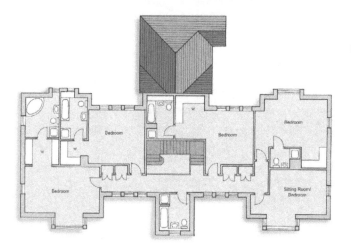

The four main bedrooms feature an en-suite bathroom each while a fifth upstairs room can double as a space for relaxation or a guest bedroom. Downstairs the L-shaped kitchen and breakfast area features plenty of storage and flows neatly into the dining room. A full-depth drawing room, family room and study complete the package.

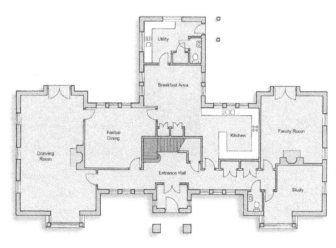

Plan no. **BHP 310644**

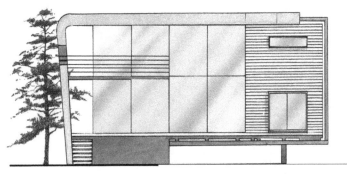

This design aims to take full advantage of a beautiful view with large areas of glass breaking down the barriers between the inside and outside. The ground floor features lots of open space but this can be changed quickly by sliding dividing screens into place. The master bedroom on the first floor features a twin aspect balcony, and is joined by another four double bedrooms.

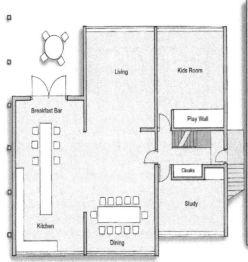

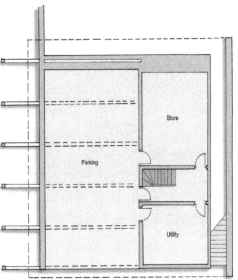

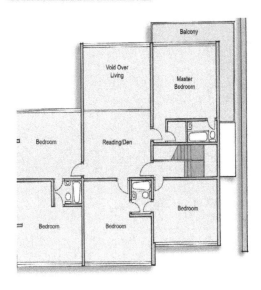

Contemporary style

Floor area
402m²
4327ft²

Bedrooms
5

Bathrooms
3

Floors
3

Key features
Open plan living
Utility room
Play room
Study
En suite master bed

Garaging for
5 cars

Design
Spacelab UK

www.spacelabuk.com
info@spacelab.co.uk
0207 684 5392

Build cost
£360,500

Design
© Spacelab UK

Traditional style

Floor area
404m²
4349ft²

Bedrooms
5

Bathrooms
4

Floors
4

Key features
Kitchen/breakfast room
Utility room
Family room
Study
Master bedroom suite

Garaging for
2 cars

Design
Design & Materials

www.designandmaterials.uk.com
enquiries@designandmaterials.uk.com
01909 540 123

Build cost
£363,000

Design
© Design & Materials

Plan no. **BHP 310056**

A sloping site doesn't mean you have to compromise on your build, in fact you can benefit from it, as this design shows. The basement effectively makes the site level and provides a double garage and covered parking for two cars along with an external and internal store. The ground and first floors are well laid out and provide ample living and sleeping space while a self-contained attic suite is a handy addition. Great glass touches including dormers, a porthole and a glazed gable add extra interest to the façade.

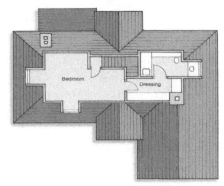

Plan no. **BHP 310641**

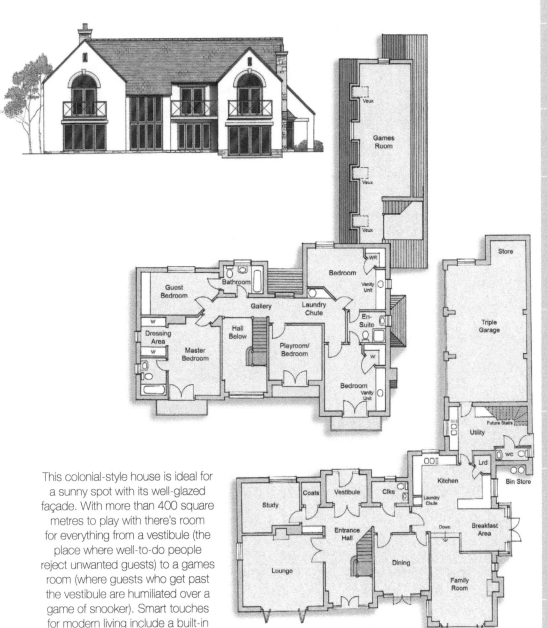

This colonial-style house is ideal for a sunny spot with its well-glazed façade. With more than 400 square metres to play with there's room for everything from a vestibule (the place where well-to-do people reject unwanted guests) to a games room (where guests who get past the vestibule are humiliated over a game of snooker). Smart touches for modern living include a built-in laundry chute and a vast utility area.

Contemporary style

Floor area
425m²
4575ft²

Bedrooms
5

Bathrooms
3

Floors
2

Key features
Kitchen/breakfast room
Family room
Study
Games Room
Master bed suite

Garaging for
3 cars

Design
Design & Materials

www.designandmaterials.uk.com
enquiries@designandmaterials.uk.com
01909 540 123

Build cost
£381,000

Contemporary style

Floor area
430m²
4628ft²

Bedrooms
5

Bathrooms
5

Floors
2

Key features
Open plan living area
Swimming pool
Music room
Conservatory
Master bedroom suite

Garaging for
2 cars

Design
Design 62

01484 300843

Build cost
£386,000

Design © Design 62

Plan no. **BHP 310068**

A spacious free flowing layout is the signature of this Design 62 house. The ground floor is largely open plan while upstairs rooms are easily accessed from the wide landing that wraps around the staircase.

Plan no. **BHP 310338**

Large families will love the balance that this house would bring to their lives. There's four similar-sized bedrooms and a fifth smaller room for a younger sibling or guest. Twin balconies at the front of the house and a vaulted ceiling to the hall add a hint of decadence to the design.

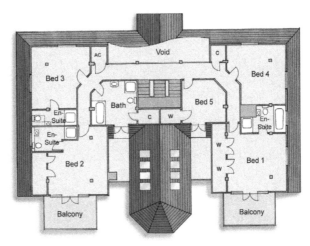

Traditional style

Floor area
450m²
4844ft²

Bedrooms
5

Bathrooms
4

Floors
2

Key features
Vaulted hall
Games Room
Full height living area
Study
3 bedrooms en suite

Garaging for
0 cars

Design
Potton

www.potton.co.uk
contact@potton.co.uk
01767 676 400

Build cost
£404,000

Design © Potton

Traditional style

Floor area
465m²
5005ft²

Bedrooms
5

Bathrooms
3

Floors
2

Key features
Kitchen/dining room
Play room
Music room
Conservatory
Master bedroom suite

Garaging for
2 cars

Design
Design & Materials

www.designandmaterials.uk.com
enquiries@designandmaterials.uk.com
01909 540 123

Build cost
£417,000

Design © Design & Materials

Plan no. **BHP 310485**

The entrance hall forms the central hub of this design with large rooms radiating outwards in three directions. Of particular note are the double-height lounge and the spacious kitchen/dining and family area. Upstairs the gallery landing mirrors the hall below and leads out to a master suite contained in its own wing. Other great features on the first floor include a sitting room, balcony and four more bedrooms.

Plan no. **BHP 310320**

Imposing in red brick this design would dominate any plot. Inside the layout goes open plan after the hallway leading into massive living spaces. The current design shows the master bedroom on the ground floor but you may decide to turn this into a self-contained guest suite and pick one of the sumptuous upstairs rooms for a master suite.

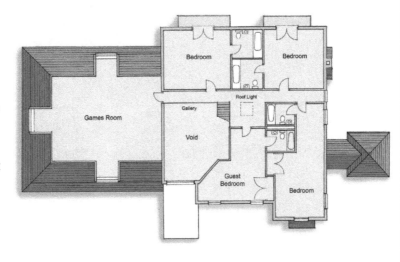

Contemporary style

Floor area
506m²
5447ft²

Bedrooms
5

Bathrooms
5

Floors
2

Key features
Kitchen/dining room
Open plan living area
Games room
Galleried landing
All bedrooms en suite

Garaging for
3 cars

Design
**John Shida
(Morningtide
Developments)**
www.morningtide.fsnet.co.uk
johnshida@morningtide.
fsnet.co.uk
01621 815485

Build cost
£454,000

Design © John Shida

Traditional style

Floor area

521m²
5608ft²

Bedrooms
5

Bathrooms
5

Floors
4

Key features
Kitchen/breakfast room
Feature staircase
Basement games room
Conservatory
Master bedroom suite

Garaging for
2 cars

Design
TJ Crump
Oakwrights

www.oakwrights.co.uk
enquiries@oakwrights.co.uk
01432 353353

Build cost
£467,000

Design © TJ Crump

Plan no. **BHP 310692**

This fabulous design from Oakwrights features four levels of living, sleeping and storage space. Neatly sandwiched between the basement garage complex and the attic level are the ground floors' massive kitchen and living room. Take the stairs up a floor and you'll find four double bedrooms and a gallery landing that overlooks a spacious entrance hall.

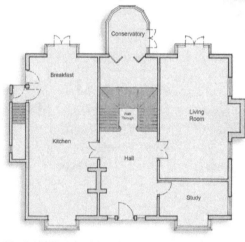

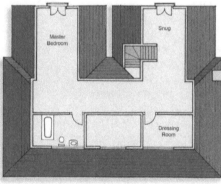

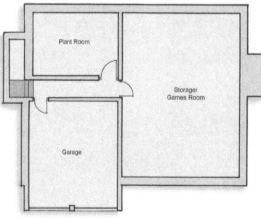

Plan no. **BHP 310815**

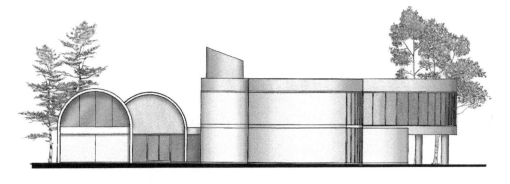

This is a startling modern design with practicality at its core. The house has a massive downstairs living space that gives you a free reign on kitchen position. Up the spiral stairs are five bedrooms off a central walkway. The dramatic round bedroom could become a fabulous feature bathroom and free up space for walk in wardrobes in the two larger bedrooms.

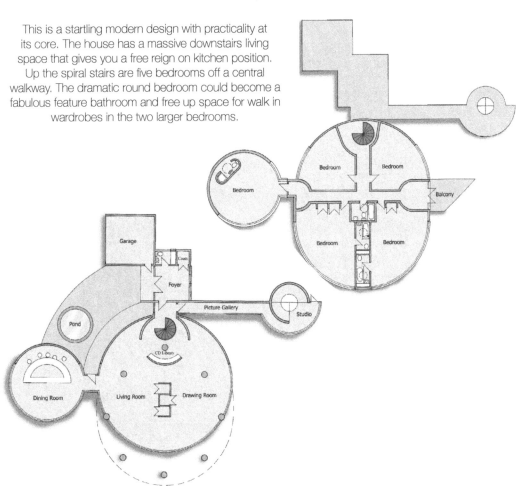

Contemporary style

Floor area
538m²
5791ft²

Bedrooms
5

Bathrooms
4

Floors
2

Key features
Kitchen/dining room
Open plan living area
Studio
Picture gallery
2 en suite beds

Garaging for
0 cars

Design
**John Shida
(Morningtide
Developments)**
www.morningtide.fsnet.co.uk
johnshida@morningtide.
fsnet.co.uk
01621 815485

Build cost
£482,500

Traditional style

Floor area
620m²
6674ft²

Bedrooms
5

Bathrooms
3

Floors
2

Key features
Kitchen/dining room
Music room
Internal courtyard
Study
All bedrooms en suite

Garaging for
2 cars

Design
**JS Building
Consultancy**

www.ukbuildingconsultancy.
co.uk
jsharples@ricsonline.org
0113 250 1303

Build cost
£556,000

Design © JS Building
Consultancy

Plan no. **BHP 310386**

Packed with palatial touches this house is impressive from every angle.
From the portico covered entry you are faced with a courtyard and a corridor
leading to a wealth of large living rooms and a big, open kitchen. The first floor
features a gallery landing leading off to five bedrooms and a balcony.

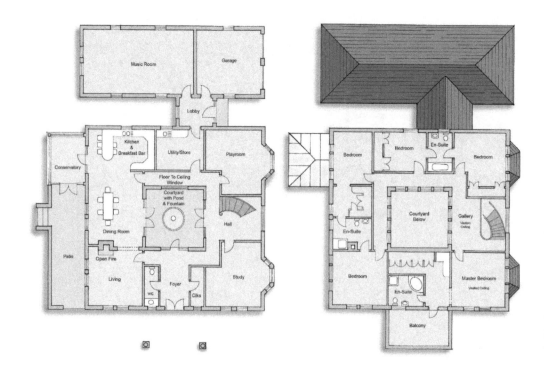

Plan no. **BHP 310161**

With an underground pool and sauna complex this house offers offers a high level features and over 650 sq m of space on a reasonably compact footprint.

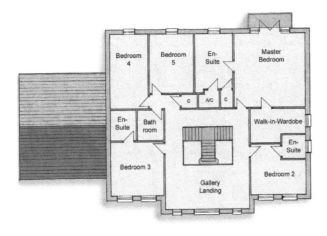

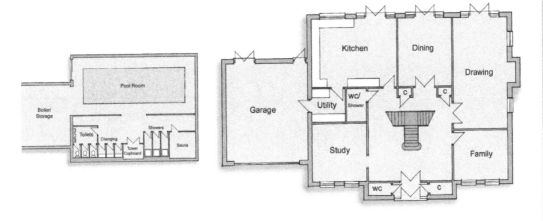

Traditional style

Floor area
668m²
7190ft²

Bedrooms
5

Bathrooms
4

Floors
3

Key features
Basement pool/sauna
Kitchen/breakfast room
Study
Separate dining room
3 bedrooms en suite

Garaging for
2 cars

Design
Custom Homes

www.customhomes.co.uk
admin@customhomes.co.uk
01787 377388

Build cost
£599,000

Design © Custom Homes

Traditional style

Floor area

698m²

7513ft²

Bedrooms

5

Bathrooms

5

Floors

2

Key features
Family room
Separate dining room
Study
Galleried landing
All bedrooms en suite

Garaging for
0 cars

Design
Border Oak

www.borderoak.com
sales@borderoak.com
01568 708752

Build cost
£626,000

Design © Border Oak

Plan no. **BHP 310188**

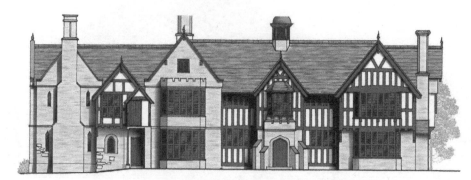

Buy yourself a title and become the lord or lady of this manor house from Border Oak. From the impressive exterior the cavernous entry hall leads into an equally large sitting room and kitchen/dining complex. The trappings of the grander life are found upstairs too where a 360 degree galleried landing takes you to five en-suite bedrooms and a playroom.

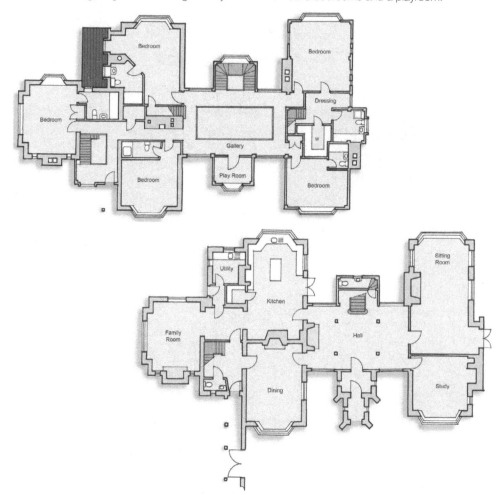

Plan no. **BHP 310971**

You can have Premiership footballer-style living for about a quarter of the price with this extravagant design from John Braid. Luxury touches include an underground pool complex and a detached car house for your Bentley and Ferrari.

Contemporary style

Floor area
850m²
9149ft²

Bedrooms
5

Bathrooms
5

Floors
3

Key features
Basement pool/gym
Kitchen/breakfast room
Billiard room
Family room
Master bedroom suite

Garaging for
3 cars

Design
John Braid
(at Leslie R Hutt)

lhuttarchitect@btinternet.com
01463 235566

Build cost
£762,000

Design © Leslie R Hutt

Floor area
218m²
2347ft²

Bedrooms
6

Bathrooms
5

Floors
2

Key features
Kitchen/dining room
Music room
Study
Larder
4 bedrooms en suite

Garaging for
2 cars

Design
Eclipse Design

www.eclipsedesign.
copperstream.co.uk
enquiries@eclipsedesignuk.
net 0845 460 4758

Build cost
£200,500

Plan no. **BHP 310881**

This traditional-looking
house is full of smart
modern advances like
the free-flowing space
between the main ground
floor rooms and an airy
feel throughout. Upstairs
there's a large balcony,
six bedrooms and five
bathrooms.

Plan no. **BHP 310773**

This imposing design is packed full of features that take it above and beyond the standard family home. The ground floor's free-flowing kitchen and dining room lead out to a covered outdoor eating area – this loggia can also be accessed from the drawing room. Upstairs there's a rear-facing balcony that leads off two bedrooms, a separate dressing room and a luxurious seating/viewing area off the landing.

Traditional style

Floor area
312m²
3358ft²

Bedrooms
6

Bathrooms
4

Floors
2

Key features
Kitchen/breakfast room
Family room
Separate dining room
Utility room
En suite master bed

Garaging for
2 cars

Design
**The Bespoke
Design Company**

www.planahome.uk.com
plans@planahome.uk.com
01326 373600

Build cost
£280,000

Design © The Bespoke
Design Company

Contemporary style

Floor area
320m²
3444ft²

Bedrooms
6

Bathrooms
4

Floors
2

Key features
Kitchen/dining room
Twin studies
Conservatory
Guest suite
Master bedroom suite

Garaging for
2 cars

Design
John Watson

Build cost
£287,000

Design © John Watson

Plan no. **BHP 310533**

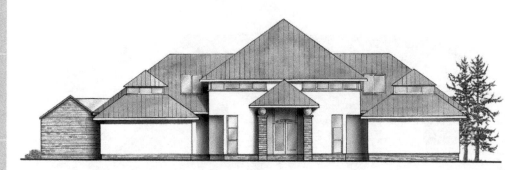

The low roofline of this house gives it the appearance of a bungalow from the outside. This could give you an advantage at the planning stage while allowing you to build a spacious two storey house. Inside the layout provides smooth transition between the living rooms while the wide landing on the first floor leads to four bedrooms and a first floor lounge.

Plan no. **BHP 310929**

Using the full height of the roof this Planahome design makes room for three floors for living and sleeping. The in-eaves bedrooms are begging to have integral balconies added to their dormer windows to take advantage of their lofty position. Downstairs there's space for any number of different room combinations but you may well want to keep the great kitchen with its integral Aga just as it is.

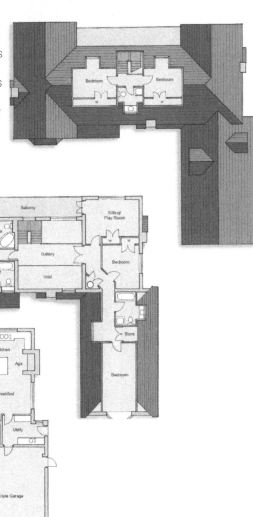

Traditional style

Floor area

336m²

3617ft²

Bedrooms

6

Bathrooms

4

Floors

3

Key features
Kitchen breakfast room
Family room
Study
Playroom
Master bed en suite

Garaging for
3 cars

Design
Planahome

www.planahome.uk.com
plans@planahome.uk.com
01326 373600

Build cost
£301,000

Design © Planahome

Traditional style

Floor area
340m²
3660ft²

Bedrooms
6

Bathrooms
3

Floors
2

Key features
Kitchen/breakfast room
Snooker room
Family room
Sun lounge
2 bedrooms en suite

Garaging for
2 cars

Design
John Braid
(at Leslie R Hutt)

lhuttarchitect@btinternet.com
01463 235566

Build cost
£305,000

Design © Leslie R Hutt

Plan no. **BHP 310095**

Among this house's luxury touches are a neat inset balcony, a double-height sun lounge to relax in and a snooker room. The master bedroom includes a sitting area as well as en suite bathroom with shower and built-in wardrobes.

Plan no. BHP 310998

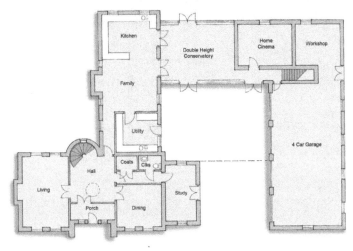

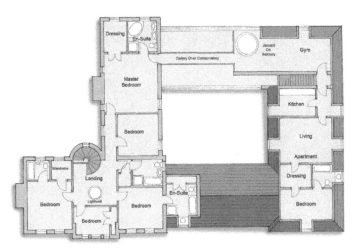

You'd expect an impressive interior after looking at this stunning façade. You won't be disappointed. Through the porch you burst into bright daylight thanks to the circular lightwell above the reception hall. The kitchen and family rooms face an enormous double height conservatory that has access both to the garden and an internal courtyard. Car fans will be delighted with the four car garage that completes the ground floor layout. Head up the circular staircase and you get access to four double bedrooms and a master suite. The master has its own walkway to the upper level of the conservatory with its jacuzzi and gym – everyone else has to take the long way round.

Traditional style

Floor area
350m²
3767ft²

Bedrooms
6

Bathrooms
5

Floors
2

Key features
Kitchen/family room
Conservatory
Study
Gym/Jacuzzi
Master bedroom suite

Garaging for
4 cars

Design
Planahome

www.planahome.uk.com
plans@planahome.uk.com
01326 373600

Build cost
£312,000

Design © Planahome

Traditional style

Floor area
436m²
4693ft²

Bedrooms
6

Bathrooms
5

Floors
2

Key features
Kitchen/family room
Conservatory
Cinema
Gym/Jacuzzi
Self-contained flat

Garaging for
4 cars

Design
Planahome

www.planahome.uk.com
plans@planahome.uk.com
01326 373600

Build cost
£391,000

Design © Planahome

Plan no. **BHP 310302**

If you've always fancied a manor house in the country this Planahome design could be just what you are looking for. Behind the impressive exterior lies a truly vast ground floor with open plan areas and private rooms for relaxation. The first floor is a study in opulence with four double bedrooms and a complete wing given over to the master suite.

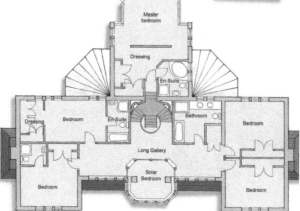

Plan no. **BHP 310785**

Traditional style

Floor area
515m²
5543ft²

Bedrooms
6

Bathrooms
5

Floors
2

This is a great family home with a garden entrance through the boot room. The reception rooms offer plenty a sapce and flexibility. Upstairs six bedrooms and five en-suite bathrooms keep the luxury levels high.

Key features
Sun lounge
Study
Family room
Separate dining room
All bedrooms en suite

Garaging for
0 cars

Design
Custom Homes

www.customhomes.co.uk
admin@customhomes.co.uk
01787 377388

Build cost
£464,500

Design © Custom Homes

Contemporary style

Floor area
550m²
5920ft²

Bedrooms
6

Bathrooms
5

Floors
3

Key features
Pool and sauna
Sun lounge
Separate dining room
Library area
Master bedroom suite

Garaging for
2 cars

Design
Design 62

01484 300843

Build cost
£493,000

Design © Design 62

Plan no. **BHP   310821**

This is a thoroughly modern mansion with luxury built in as standard. Twin, double-height, conservatories sit on either side of the house and pump light into a ground floor with space for a jacuzzi, sauna and a pool. Upstairs the conservatories add light to the larger bedroom at one end and provide a stunning view-point seating area at the other.

Plan no. **BHP 310125**

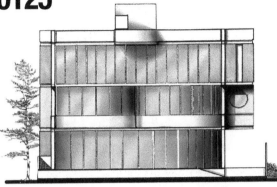

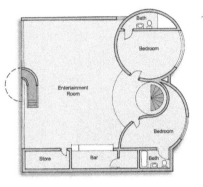

As much a leisure complex as a home this study in circles from John Shida is designed to impress. The entire basement is taken over by a pool, gym and jacuzzi. Upstairs the ground floor features a playroom along with an open plan living and dining area. The leisure theme continues on the first floor with its dedicated, full-depth, entertainment room and ends with a flourish on the second floor's circular deck.

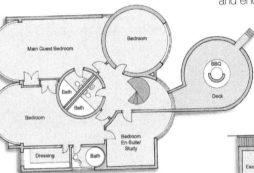

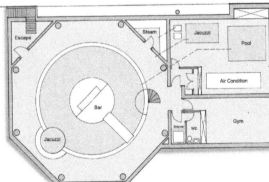

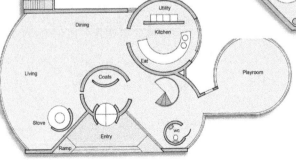

Contemporary style

Floor area
888m²
9558ft²

Bedrooms
6

Bathrooms
5

Floors
4

Key features
Swimming pool/gym
Open plan living area
Entertainment room
BBQ deck
Playroom

Garaging for
0 cars

Design
**John Shida
(Morningtide
Developments)**
www.morningtide.fsnet.co.uk
johnshida@morningtide.
fsnet.co.uk
01621 815485

Build cost
£796,000

Design © John Shida

Traditional style

Floor area
236m²
2540ft²

Bedrooms
7

Bathrooms
4

Floors
3

Key features
Kitchen/breakfast room
Conservatory
Separate dining room
Games room
3 en suites

Garaging for
0 cars

Design
Potton

www.potton.co.uk
contact@potton.co.uk
01767 676 400

Build cost
£212,000

Design © Potton

Plan no. **BHP 310185**

Three floors means more than 230 square metres can be built into this Potton house. There's a great layout for living on the ground floor while the first and second floors provide five bedrooms and a games room.

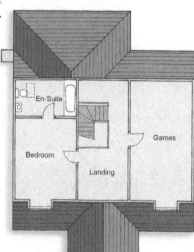

Plan no. BHP 310440

Taking the L-shape Design to the max is this six bed design from Planahome. In this brick and part-timber finish there's plenty of hints of old England but stone or block and render could be used to allow this house to fit in with the local built environment. There's a guest suite built into the eaves at one end of the house and a fully self-contained living space above the triple garage with its own staircase.

Traditional style

Floor area
332m²
3574ft²

Bedrooms
7

Bathrooms
4

Floors
2

Key features
Kitchen/breakfast room
Dining hall
Family room
Utility room
Master bedroom suite

Garaging for
3 cars

Design
Planahome

www.planahome.uk.com
plans@planahome.uk.com
01326 373600

Build cost
£298,000

Design © Planahome

Traditional style

Floor area
354m²
3810ft²

Bedrooms
7

Bathrooms
4

Floors
3

Key features
Kitchen/breakfast room
Family room
Separate dining room
Library
Master bedroom suite

Garaging for
2 cars

Design
Planahome

www.planahome.uk.com
plans@planahome.uk.com
01326 373600

Build cost
£317,500

Design © Planahome

Plan no. **BHP 310305**

This design offers a comfortable large family home. The entrance hall is designed to impress and the master bedroom has a large dressing area and en suite bathroom.

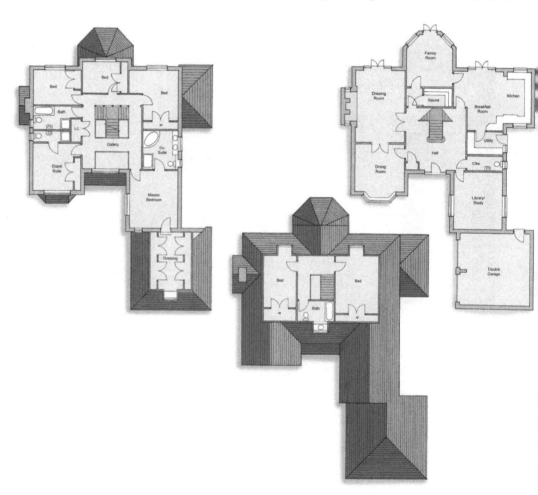

Plan no. **BHP 310848**

This magnificent home stables as well as integral garaging and a swimming pool cin an enormous conservatory. Upstairs is similarly luxurious with a galleried landingand a substantial master bedroom suite with separare study and snug.

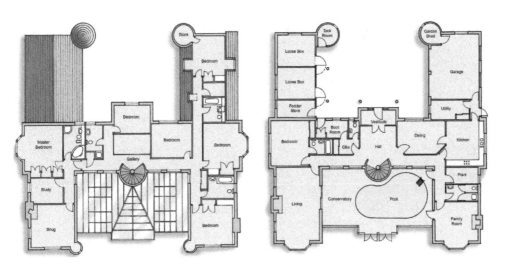

Contemporary style

Floor area
454m²
4887ft²

Bedrooms
6

Bathrooms
7

Floors
1

Key features
Swimming pool
Open plan living area
Conservatory
Library
6 bedrooms en suite

Garaging for
2 cars

Design
Architecture Plus

www.architecture-plus.co.uk
01934 416416

Build cost
£407,000

Design © Architecture Plus

Plan no. **BHP 310344**

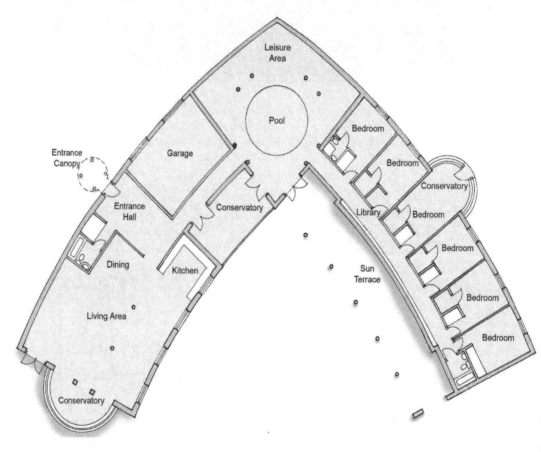

Like the bow of a vast ocean-going liner this design dominates its surroundings and provides luxury living for its inhabitants. The pool area forms the central hub of the house and leads off to six en-suite bedrooms and a sun terrace to starboard and an open plan kitchen/dining area on the port side. Three conservatories are included in the design to take advantage of morning, midday and afternoon sun.

Plan no. **BHP 310674**

The compact footprint of this house and the use of a basement initially hides the fact that it offers a massive 511 sq m of living space - allowing for seven bedrooms as well as swimming pool and gym.

Contemporary style

Floor area
511m²
5500ft²

Bedrooms
7

Bathrooms
4

Floors
4

Key features
Swimming pool/gym
Kitchen/breakfast room
Living/dining room
Study
4 bedrooms en suite

Garaging for
0 cars

Design
Design & Materials

www.designandmaterials.uk.com
enquiries@designandmaterials.uk.com
01909 540 123

Build cost
£458,000

Design © Design & Materials

Traditional style

Floor area
545 m²
5866 ft²

Bedrooms
7

Bathrooms
7

Floors
2

Key features
Full height 'Great Hall'
Kitchen/breakfast room
Family room
Library
All bedrooms en suite

Garaging for
0 cars

Design
Jeremy Rawlings

www.periodhome.net
01884 266444

Build cost
£489,000

Plan no. **BHP 310611**

There's an ecclesiastical air to this design thanks to its mullioned windows and grand, arched entrance. Inside, things are less church-like but still divine with enormous ground floor rooms separated by wide-opening twin doors offering brilliant flexibility. The first floor offers six bedrooms in the current layout but as with downstairs, there's so much space you'll have plenty of options.

Plan no. **BHP 310638**

This character-packed house doesn't waste a centimetre of space to deliver the ideal living environment. The kitchen, conservatory and breakfast area are ergonomically perfect for a busy family while the various sitting areas and pool supply room for relaxation too. Upstairs there are balconies for three of the bedrooms, a gallery landing and a vaulted-ceiling sitting area.

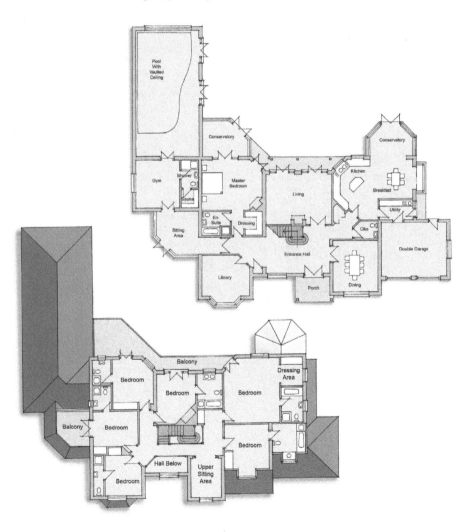

Traditional style

Floor area
558m²
6006 ft²

Bedrooms
7

Bathrooms
7

Floors
2

Key features
Swimming pool/Gym
Kitchen/breakfast room
Library
Conservatory
All bedrooms en suite

Garaging for
2 cars

Design
Design & Materials

www.designandmaterials.uk.com
enquiries@designandmaterials.uk.com
01909 540 123

Build cost
£500,500

Design
© Design & Materials

Traditional style

Floor area
576m²
6200ft²

Bedrooms
7

Bathrooms
6

Floors
2

Key features
Kitchen dining room
Conservatory
Playroom
Vaulted sitting room
Self-contained flat

Garaging for
3 cars

Design
Design & Materials

www.designandmaterials.uk.com
enquiries@designandmaterials.
uk.com
01909 540 123

Build cost
£516,500

Design © Design &
Materials

Plan no. **BHP 310287**

If one house can show the benefits that self build can have on your wallet then this is it. Find a big enough plot and you could build this near 600 square metre house for just over £500,000. For that you get seven bedrooms, more en-suites than you can shake a stick at and enormous ground floor living spaces.

Plan no. **BHP 310119**

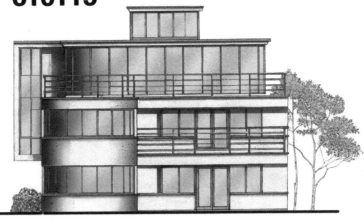

Art Deco influences abound in this design from Architecture Plus. The layout is based around a central lightwell which is surrounded by a gallery and a staircase rising between levels. The first and second floors have access to balconies and the open-plan ground floor lounge features a splendid semi-circular bay window.

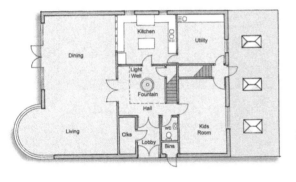

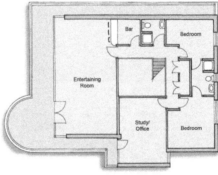

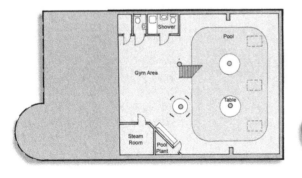

Contemporary style

Floor area
635m²
6835 ft²

Bedrooms
7

Bathrooms
6

Floors
4

Key features
Swimming pool/gym
Open plan living area
Entertaing room
Study
Master bedroom suite

Garaging for
0 cars

Design
Architecture Plus

www.architecture-plus.co.uk
01934 416416

Build cost
£569,500

Design © Architecture Plus

Contemporary style

Floor area
700 m²
7535 ft²

Bedrooms
7

Bathrooms
4

Floors
4

Key features
Swimming pool/gym
Entertaining room
Living/Dining room
Playroom
Master bedroom suite

Garaging for
0 cars

Design
Jeremy Rawlings

www.periodhome.net
01884 266444

Build cost
£628,000

Design
© Jeremy Rawlings

Plan no. **BHP 310335**

Jeremy Rawlings has put the drama back
in to design with his outstanding take on
the family home. Glass, concrete and wood
combine to create the shape which contains
four floors of living and sleeping space.
Outside space is carefully considered too with
a full-width deck on the ground floor and offset
balconies on the first and second floors.

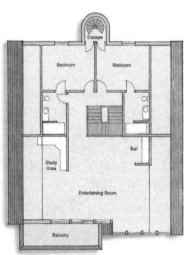

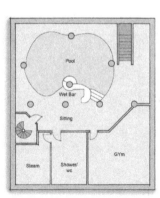

Plan no. **BHP 310299**

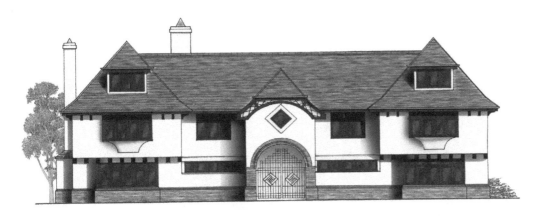

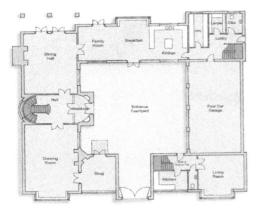

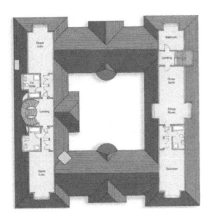

If you have a very large family, or just like to spread out, this could be the home for you. The four sides of the house form a central entrance courtyard. Choose your entrance: through the four car garage if you're driving or into an impressive entrance vestibule if you're walking. Once inside the scale of the house will amaze you. Three separate staircases take you to the first floor with its array of bedrooms, bathrooms, gallery and study. The central staircase spirals upwards to the second floor landing's guest suites. On the opposite side of the house there's another guest suite and two further bedrooms.

Traditional style

Floor area
880m²
9472 ft²

Bedrooms
12

Bathrooms
8

Floors
3

Key features
Entrance courtyard
Kitchen/family room
Dining hall
Guest bedroom suite
Master bedroom suite

Garaging for
4 cars

Design
**The Bespoke
Design Company**

www.planahome.uk.com
plans@planahome.uk.com
01326 373600

**Build cost
£789,000**

For the best building books

THEBUILDINGSITE.COM

www.thebuildingsite.com